P9-BYQ-590

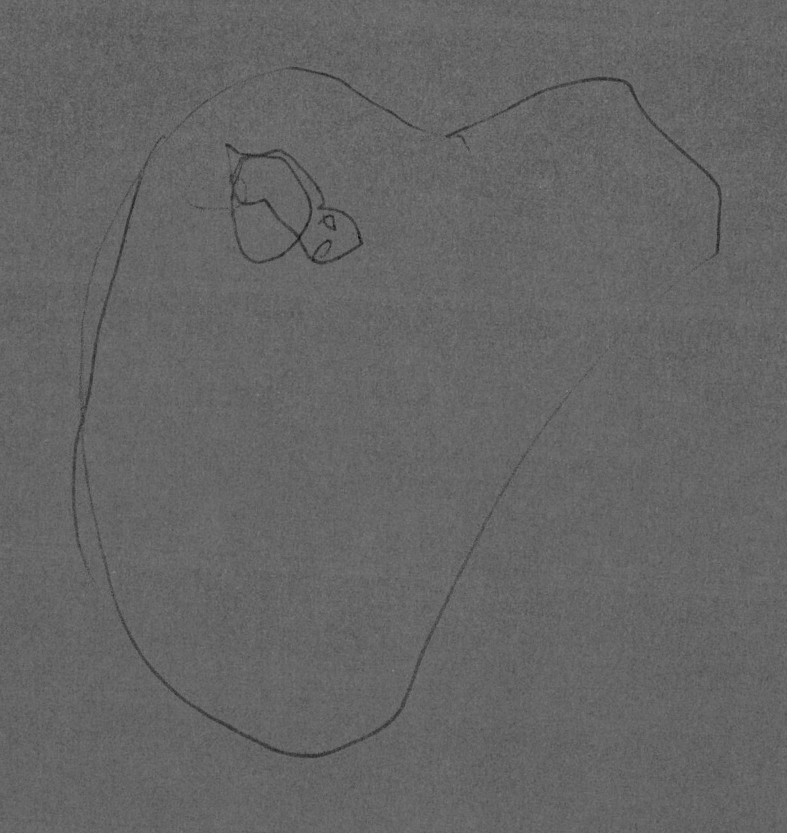

Tony Tallarico

Kidsbooks®

3535 West Peterson Avenue
Chicago, IL 60659

Printed in the United States of America

011004003OH

Visit us at **www.kidsbooks.com®**

DINOSAURS LOST IN TIME

I FEEL A LITTLE SHAKY! I WANT MY MAMA DIPLODOCUS!
ONE WAY
I'M A COELOPHYSIS, AND I'M SCARED!
IGUANODON OUT OF HERE!
NO EXIT
CHECK THIS OUT!
DON'T STOP NOW
I LIKE TO SHAKE, RATTLE, AND ROLL!
I'M A DEINONYCHUS.
BERNIE WAS HERE
DON'T KEEP OUT!
DON'T READ THIS.
DON'T COME IN!
DON'T STAND STILL.
WHO ARE THEY?
I HAVEN'T BEEN INVENTED YET!
OR ME!
COMPSOGNATHUS WANTS TO GO HOME!!

"Check this out!" said Apatosaurus *(uh-PAT-uh-SORE-us)* to his dinosaur friends. "It's the weirdest cave I've ever seen." They all stepped in, and the strange cave began to shake and spin through time. "Whoa!" they shouted, as they landed in the present day. Can you find some of the things they saw?

- ❑ Banana peel
- ❑ Bat
- ❑ Book
- ❑ Broom
- ❑ Can
- ❑ Candle
- ❑ Chair
- ❑ Coffeepot
- ❑ Fire hydrant
- ❑ Fish
- ❑ Football
- ❑ Fork
- ❑ Hammer
- ❑ Heart
- ❑ Hot dog
- ❑ House
- ❑ Key
- ❑ Kite
- ❑ Mouse
- ❑ Paintbrush
- ❑ Pencil
- ❑ Rabbit
- ❑ Saw
- ❑ Ship
- ❑ Star
- ❑ Umbrella
- ❑ Wagon

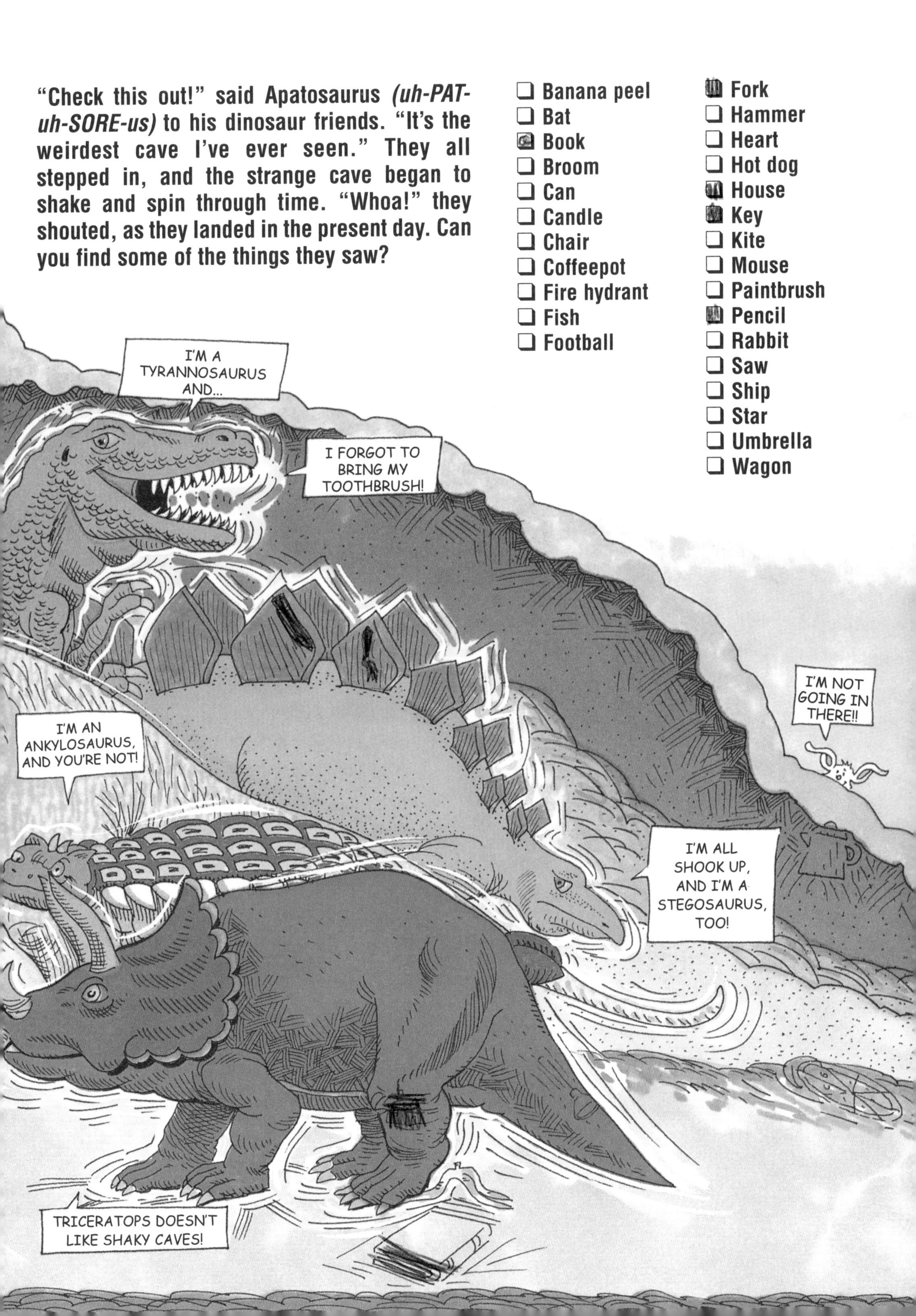

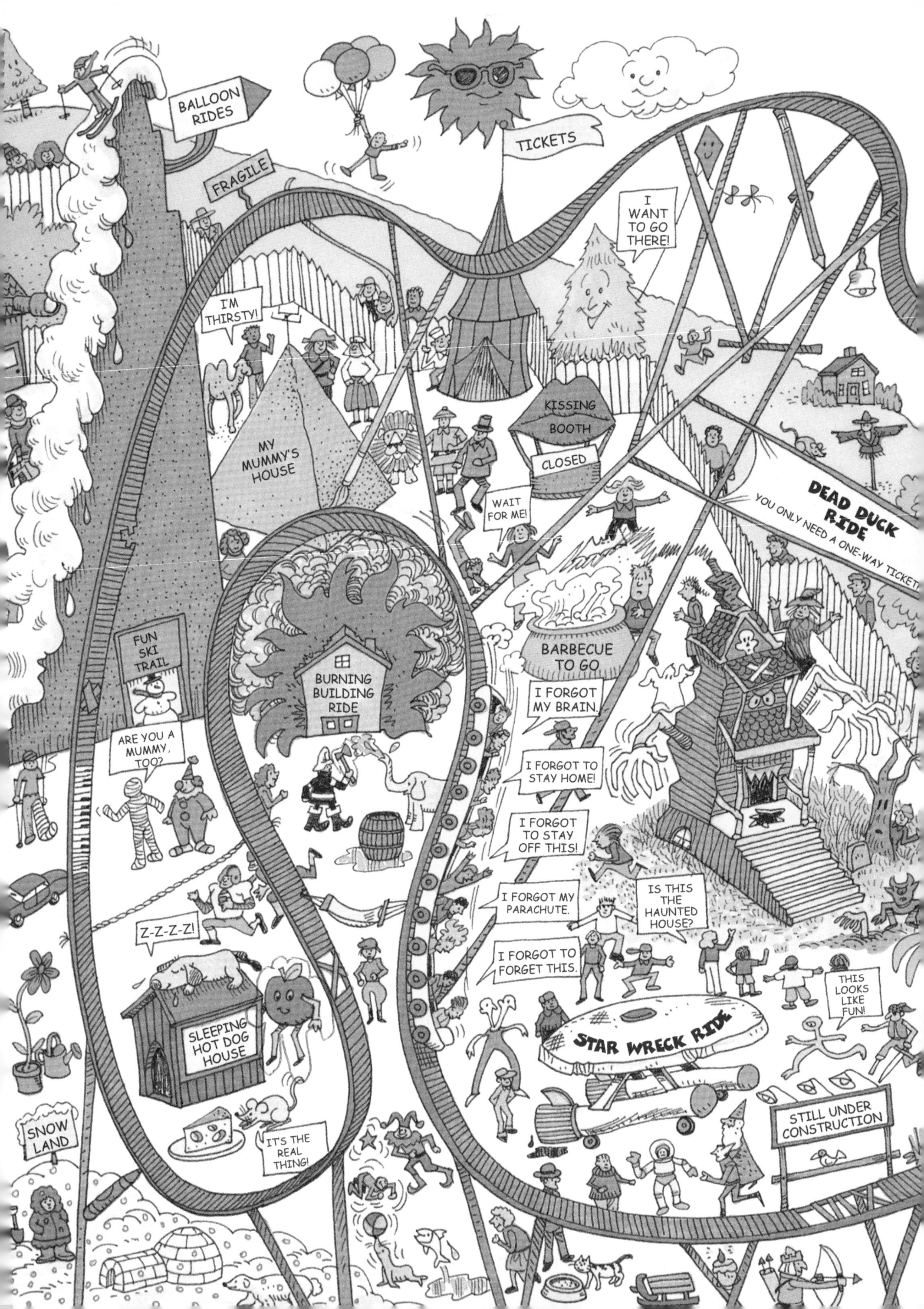
BALLOON RIDES
TICKETS
FRAGILE
I WANT TO GO THERE!
I'M THIRSTY!
MY MUMMY'S HOUSE
KISSING BOOTH
CLOSED
DEAD DUCK RIDE
YOU ONLY NEED A ONE-WAY TICKET!
WAIT FOR ME!
BARBECUE TO GO
FUN SKI TRAIL
BURNING BUILDING RIDE
I FORGOT MY BRAIN.
ARE YOU A MUMMY, TOO?
I FORGOT TO STAY HOME!
I FORGOT TO STAY OFF THIS!
I FORGOT MY PARACHUTE.
IS THIS THE HAUNTED HOUSE?
Z-Z-Z-Z!
I FORGOT TO FORGET THIS.
THIS LOOKS LIKE FUN!
SLEEPING HOT DOG HOUSE
STAR WRECK RIDE
STILL UNDER CONSTRUCTION
SNOW LAND
IT'S THE REAL THING!

"I wonder where we are," said Apatosaurus. "Why don't we split up and check it out?" They agreed, and decided to meet back at the cave at the end of their adventurous day. Can you find Apatosaurus at this carnival, along with the other fun things listed below?

- [x] Alarm clock
- [x] Apple
- [x] Axe
- [ ] Bell
- [ ] Bones (2)
- [ ] Butterfly
- [ ] Candle
- [ ] Chef
- [ ] Crayon
- [ ] Elephant
- [ ] Ghost
- [ ] Hammock
- [ ] Knight
- [ ] Mice (3)
- [ ] Paintbrush
- [ ] Paint bucket
- [ ] Pencil
- [ ] Piano keys
- [ ] Skull
- [ ] Snake
- [ ] Snowman
- [ ] Stilts
- [ ] Turtle
- [ ] TV antennas (2)
- [ ] Two-headed alien
- [ ] Unicorn

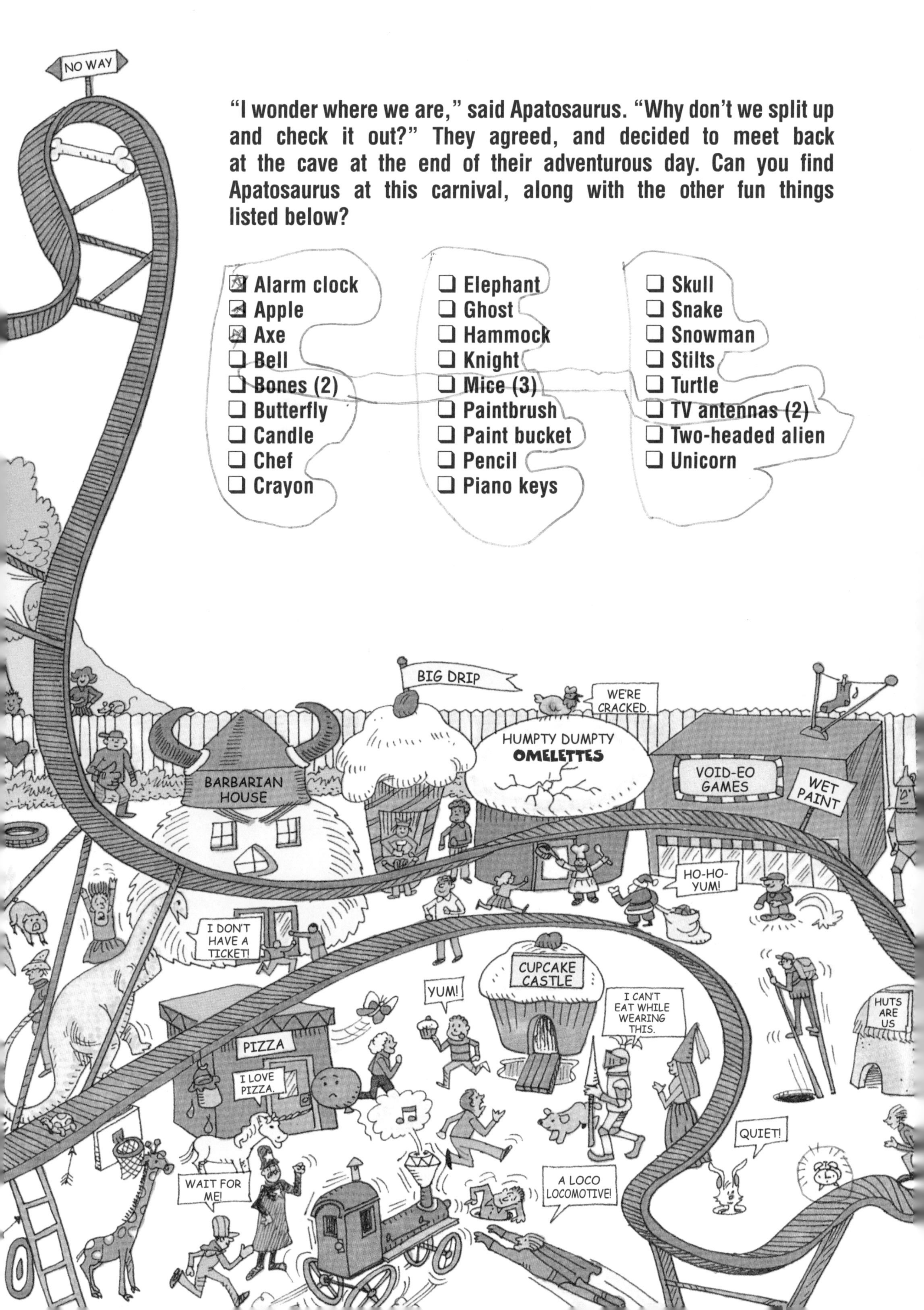

I'M GOING TO HAVE THIS CALLED OFF ON ACCOUNT OF RAIN.
THIS IS A GREAT IDEA.
THIS MUST BE THE PLACE.
I WANT TO JOIN THE BAND.
I'M GLAD I CAN'T SEE THEM.
IS ELVIS HERE?
THIS ISN'T THE ZOO!
I LOST MY BRUSH!
THEY SHOULDN'T QUIT THEIR DAY JOBS.
TOTALLY AWESOME!
DID YOU LOSE THIS?
COOL!
I LIKE IT COOL!
I'LL TAKE ONE FOR EACH ARM.
HOT-DOGS!
I PREFER COUNTRY MUSIC.

“This place sounds really crazy,” said Compsognathus *(komp-sog-NAY-thus)*. “I wonder what’s going on?” Can you find Apatosaurus and Compsognathus at this rock concert? Don’t forget to look for the following fun things, too.

- ❑ Belt
- ❑ Birdcage
- ❑ Candle
- ❑ Chef’s hat
- ❑ Chicken drumstick
- ❑ Crown
- ❑ Elephant
- ❑ Fish
- ❑ Hammer
- ❑ Heart
- ❑ Hot-air balloon
- ❑ Ice-cream cone
- ❑ Mermaid
- ❑ Mouse
- ❑ Octopus
- ❑ Owl
- ❑ Paper airplane
- ❑ Pencil
- ❑ Pie
- ❑ Rabbit
- ❑ Saw
- ❑ Skate
- ❑ Snail
- ❑ Sock
- ❑ Star
- ❑ Turtle
- ❑ Worm

IT'S AS COLD AS THE ICE AGE HERE.
RINK EATERY
WE SELL FROZEN FOODS!
I'M WORKING LIKE A DOG!
WAITER!
CONDO FOR SALE
THE REAL FOOD IS DOWN THERE!
HO-HO-HUH?
WHAT IS THAT?
ARE YOU ON THE HOCKEY TEAM?
THIS IS MY NEW SKATING COSTUME.
SMILE!
WHO NEEDS SKATES?
I THINK I FORGOT SOMETHING!
THE ICE IS SLIPPERY!
OOPS! WRONG SKATES!
WE'RE LOST!
HELP!
JUST WHEN YOU THOUGHT IT WAS SAFE TO GO ON THE ICE AGAIN...
I'M A RING ON THE RINK!
I TELL YOU, I SAW THREE DINOSAURS!
THAT MUST HAVE BEEN A HARD CROSS-CHECK.
ARE WE ON TV?
DID U READ THIS?
POST NO BILLS! COINS ONLY!
DO NOT FEED THE SKATERS!
KEEP ON THE ICE
SOMETIMES THIN ICE
DINOSAURS NOT PERMITTED ON THE ICE!

"Oh, cool! But where am I?" said Triceratops *(try-SER-uh-tops)*. "Hey! I see some of my friends." Can you find Apatosaurus, Triceratops, and Compsognathus at this skating rink? Don't forget to look for the following fun things, too.

- ❑ Alligator
- ❑ Bone
- ❑ Bowling ball
- ❑ Broom
- ❑ Cactuses (2)
- ❑ Cameras (2)
- ❑ Crutch
- ❑ Elf
- ❑ Football player
- ❑ Humpty Dumpty
- ❑ Hungry monster
- ❑ Ice skateboard
- ❑ Igloo
- ❑ Kangaroo
- ❑ Lost mitten
- ❑ Mouse
- ❑ Necklace
- ❑ Panda
- ❑ Penguins (2)
- ❑ Pillow
- ❑ Roller skates
- ❑ Santa Claus
- ❑ Shark fin
- ❑ Skier
- ❑ Straw basket
- ❑ Telescope
- ❑ TV set

WE COOK 'EM YOU EAT 'EM!! FAST FOOD
AN ESCAPED BALLOON!
SLOW TODAY!
WHO GETS THE SPECIAL?
HOW'S BUSINESS?
I DO!
HOT CHILI
FRIES
BURGERS
PIZZA
HOT DOGS
SHAKES
SLURP!
I WANT MY BUGER RAW!
I'M NEXT!
THEY'RE GIVING THESE AWAY TODAY!
HEY! GET YOUR OWN!
TAKE ME TO YOUR LEADER!
IT'S BUNNYMAN!
IT'S RAINING HOT CHOCOLATE!
I WANT TO EAT AT HOME!
I'M GOING TO OPEN A FAST-FOOD STAND WHEN I GET BACK HOME.
I DON'T EAT!
THIS PLACE IS CROWDED TODAY.
I EAT HERE, TOO!
IT'S NOT CROWDED.
TO GO

"Yum! Something smells good," said Iguanodon *(ih-GWAHN-uh-don)*. "Maybe I'll give up eating plants." Can you find Apatosaurus, Triceratops, Compsognathus, and Iguanodon at this fast-food stand? Don't forget to look for the following fun things, too.

- ❑ Apple
- ❑ Astronaut
- ❑ Candy cane
- ❑ Chicken
- ❑ Clown
- ❑ Count Dracula
- ❑ Diver
- ❑ Doctor
- ❑ Dog
- ❑ Doughnut
- ❑ Duck
- ❑ Fish
- ❑ Monster
- ❑ Moose head
- ❑ Mouse
- ❑ Mustache
- ❑ Penguin
- ❑ Pinocchio
- ❑ Propeller
- ❑ Seal
- ❑ Star
- ❑ Straws (2)
- ❑ Surfer
- ❑ Torn bag
- ❑ Turtle
- ❑ Unicycle
- ❑ Viking

THE BIG FISH AQUARIUM
SALE
I FORGOT WHAT I CAME HERE FOR.
I NEVER SAW THIS BEFORE.
MALL MOVIES
SNOW SALE
SHOP MORE
HAVE A NICE DAY
FUNNY FARM MALL
THIS IS BETTER THAN WALKING.
KIDS' BOOK-STORE
DOWN
YOU HAVE BAD BREATH!
HI!
I DON'T SEE GRANDMA!
I'M GLAD WE BECAME FRIENDS.
PORTRAITS $25.00
SHOP 'TIL U DROP
I'M OVER-STUFFED.
SALE
STUFFED TOYS TENT
ME, TOO!
IT'S REAL!
IT'S SO CUTE!
HE LOOKS LIKE UNCLE MAXWELL.
YIPES!
IT WORKS!
BUY ME
WOOF! GET ME OUT OF HERE!
SLIPPERY WHEN WET

"This place is out of control. I see some of my friends, but who's that dino?" said Stegosaurus *(STEG-uh-SORE-us)*, looking at a toy dinosaur. Can you find Apatosaurus, Compsognathus, Triceratops, Iguanodon, and Stegosaurus at this shopping mall? Don't forget to look for the following fun things, too.

- ❑ Artist
- ❑ Basketball
- ❑ Birdbath
- ❑ Book
- ❑ Broken window
- ❑ Bubble gum
- ❑ Caveman
- ❑ Cup
- ❑ Fire hydrant
- ❑ Flower
- ❑ Guitar
- ❑ Hammer
- ❑ Hammerhead shark
- ❑ Hearts (3)
- ❑ Paddleball
- ❑ Pig
- ❑ Sale signs (4)
- ❑ Secret agent
- ❑ Shoeless girl
- ❑ Snowman
- ❑ Star
- ❑ Stuffed bear
- ❑ Toy dino
- ❑ Toy truck
- ❑ Volcano
- ❑ Yo-yo

CLASS TRIP
DON'T LOOK UP HERE!
SPITBALL DETECTOR
JURASSIC BIRD
PTEROSAUR
I'M LATE!
I'M GETTING OUT OF HERE!
I'M ON A CALENDAR.
THIS IS MY SCIENCE EXPERIMENT.
I'VE BEEN HERE SINCE LAST WINTER.
ME, TOO!
F
TO BE OR NOT TO BE.
UH-OH!
I HAVE TO TRIM OFF A DEAD LEAF!
TO ACT OR NOT TO ACT— THAT IS MY QUESTION TO YOU!
I THINK WE'RE DRESSED FOR THE WRONG SCHOOL PLAY!
71

"Look at all those little creatures! They seem to know where they're going," said Diplodocus *(dih-PLOH-duh-kus)*. "Maybe they can tell me where I am." Can you find Apatosaurus, Compsognathus, Triceratops, Iguanodon, Stegosaurus, and Diplodocus? Don't forget to look for the following fun things, too.

- ❑ Airplane
- ❑ Apple
- ❑ Arrow
- ❑ Balloons (3)
- ❑ Baseball
- ❑ Calendar
- ❑ Carrot
- ❑ Cat
- ❑ Coonskin cap
- ❑ Crown
- ❑ Elephant
- ❑ Football helmet
- ❑ Golf club
- ❑ Hockey stick
- ❑ Kites (2)
- ❑ Lunch box
- ❑ Oilcan
- ❑ Pyramid
- ❑ Rocket ship
- ❑ Roller skate
- ❑ Sailor cap
- ❑ Scissors
- ❑ Straw
- ❑ Unicorn
- ❑ Van
- ❑ Watering can

NICE CROWD TODAY.
THAT'S MY OLD TAXI.
DID SOMEONE CALL ME?
OOPS!
I READ THE BOOK HE WAS IN.
CAN YOU DIRECT ME TO THE WATER FOUNTAIN?
I'M NOT A PAINTING.
GONE FISHING!
KNOCK, KNOCK!
STOP LOOKING AT ME!
WHERE DID YOU GET THAT HAT?
HAVE YOU SEEN THE MAD HATTER?
?
I FEEL LIKE A BULL IN A CHINA CLOSET.
YOU'RE OLDER THAN I AM.
I'M AN ARTIST.
OOPS! SORRY.
WHERE'S SANTA?
DID SOMEONE CALL ME?
LOVELY.
I THINK HE PLAYED SOCCER.
I THINK HE WORKED IN OUR SCHOOL LUNCHROOM.
WHAT DOES "RABBIT" MEAN?

"Apatosaurus, Apatosaurus!" shouted Coelophysis (SEEL-uh-FYE-sis) to the statue. "Sorry, I thought you were my friend." Can you find Apatosaurus, Triceratops, Compsognathus, Iguanodon, Stegosaurus, Diplodocus, and Coelophysis at this amusing museum? Don't forget to look for the following fun things, too.
❑ Bird
❑ Boot
❑ Bowling ball
❑ Chef
❑ Fish
❑ Flying carpet
❑ Frog
❑ Hammer
❑ Headless body
❑ Ice-cream cone
❑ Jack-o'-lantern
❑ Light bulb
❑ Mouse
❑ Mummy
❑ Pencil
❑ Periscope
❑ Piggy bank
❑ Pyramid
❑ Roller skates
❑ Rubber ducky
❑ Saw
❑ Screwdriver
❑ Soccer ball
❑ Swan
❑ Swords (2)
❑ Tic-tac-toe
❑ Tree stump
❑ Turtle
❑ TV antenna
❑ Upside-down picture
IS IT STRAIGHT?
PIZZA!
IF THAT FALLS ON ME, I'M GOING TO FLY AWAY!
WHAT'S COOKING?
IT LOOKS STRAIGHT!
GREAT!
I WONDER IF IT EATS BIRDSEED?
I DO!
I LEFT SOMETHING AT HOME.
I ALWAYS TAKE A BATH ON SATURDAY NIGHT.
I WENT TO THE BANK!
I'M HITTING THE ROAD.
WHERE'S THE ABSTRACT ART?

SMILE!
FOR RENT.
I'M THE ZOO'S WACKY WALRUS!
I DON'T HIBERNATE.
OOOPS!
THEY'RE STRANGE-LOOKING.
I'M A BABY BELUGA.
TAKE ME TO YOUR LEADER.
HE LOOKS SOMETHING LIKE A MAMMOTH!
WE'RE LOST.
I'M AN AUSTRALIAN FOOTBALL STAR.
HAVE YOU SEEN ANY OTHER DINOS?
I'M A LLAMA.
ICE CREAM
CAN I HAVE A LICK?
YUM!
I'M A VICUNA.
I'M A FLAMINGO.
THAT'S AN "EGGSTRAVAGANZA!"
HAPPY BIRTHDAY!
RUN!! THAT'S AN ANTEATER!
I'M A BABY ALLIGATOR AND YOU'RE NOT!
WHAT DOES "TIMBER" MEAN?
HELP!
"OH GIVE ME A HOME WHERE THE BUFFALO ROAM..."
DON'T CALL ME A BUFFALO!
I JUST BECAME A FATHER.
OK. YOU'RE A BISON.
IS THAT ME, OR HIS SINGING?
TIMBER!
I LOVE FOSSILS.

"I don't like this place at all," said Deinonychus *(dyne-ON-ik-us)*. "There are too many strange creatures. I'm getting out of here quick." Can you find Apatosaurus, Triceratops, Compsognathus, Iguanodon, Stegosaurus, Diplodocus, Coelophysis, and Deinonychus at this zoo? Don't forget to look for the following fun things, too.

- ❑ Aardvark
- ❑ Alien
- ❑ Anteater
- ❑ Arrow
- ❑ Baseball glove
- ❑ Bat
- ❑ Beaver
- ❑ Bighorn
- ❑ Bottle
- ❑ Butterfly
- ❑ Candle
- ❑ Clown
- ❑ Dog
- ❑ Duck
- ❑ Kangaroo
- ❑ Lost balloon
- ❑ Moose
- ❑ Net
- ❑ Owls (2)
- ❑ Panda
- ❑ Polar bear
- ❑ Raccoon
- ❑ Rhinoceros
- ❑ Sick animal
- ❑ Singing cactus
- ❑ Snakes (2)
- ❑ Toucan
- ❑ Umbrellas (3)
- ❑ Wolf
- ❑ Yak

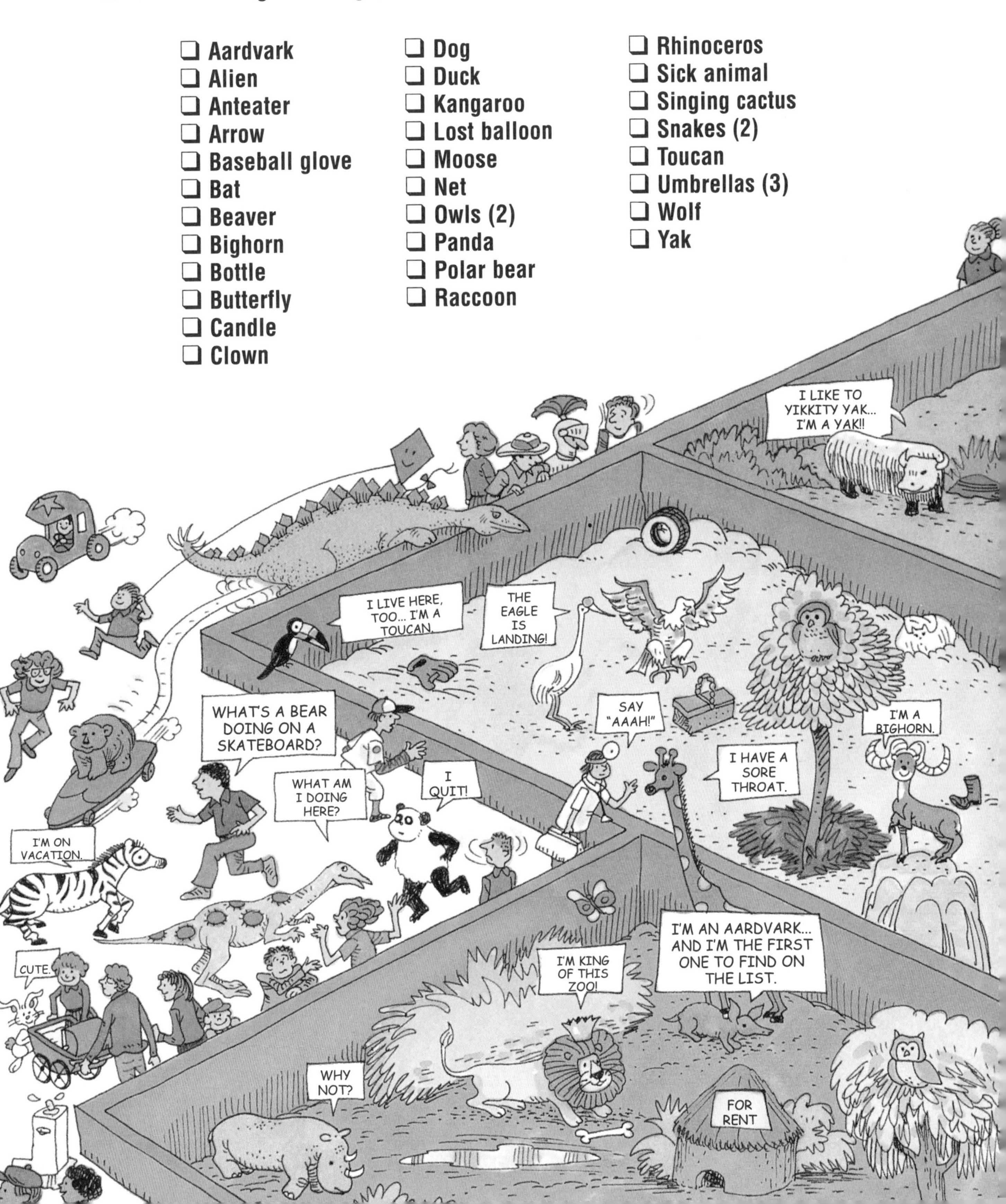

IT'S NOT REAL!
I'D LIKE LIVING HERE FOR GOOD.
I'M A BOOK-WORM.
THAT TICKLES!
ONE TOY PIZZA, TO GO!
DO YOU HAVE CHEESE?
ARE THEY CHOCOLATE CHIP?
I CAN'T EAT WEARING THIS COSTUME!!
THOSE COOKIES LOOK GOOD!
H-E-L-P Y-O-U-R-S-E-L-F!
HOWDY.
I'M NOT!
I'M ON A DIET!

"Hey, this place is wild!" said Tyrannosaurus *(tye-RAN-uh-SORE-us)*. "This guy looks just like me, but why is he so small?" Can you find Apatosaurus, Triceratops, Compsognathus, Iguanodon, Stegosaurus, Diplodocus, Coelophysis, Deinonychus, and Tyrannosaurus at this toy store? Don't forget to look for the following fun things, too.

- ❑ Anchor
- ❑ Arrow
- ❑ Basketball
- ❑ Blimp
- ❑ Block
- ❑ Bow ties (3)
- ❑ Camel
- ❑ Carrot
- ❑ Cars (4)
- ❑ Crown
- ❑ Dart
- ❑ Duck cap
- ❑ Fishing pole
- ❑ Ghost
- ❑ Golf club
- ❑ Jack-in-the-box
- ❑ Mask
- ❑ Mouse
- ❑ Mushroom
- ❑ Palm tree
- ❑ Pencil
- ❑ Piggy bank
- ❑ Robot waiter
- ❑ Rocking chair
- ❑ Skate
- ❑ Skeleton
- ❑ Tepee
- ❑ Unicorn
- ❑ Whistle
- ❑ Wind-up volcano
- ❑ Yo-yo
- ❑ Zebra

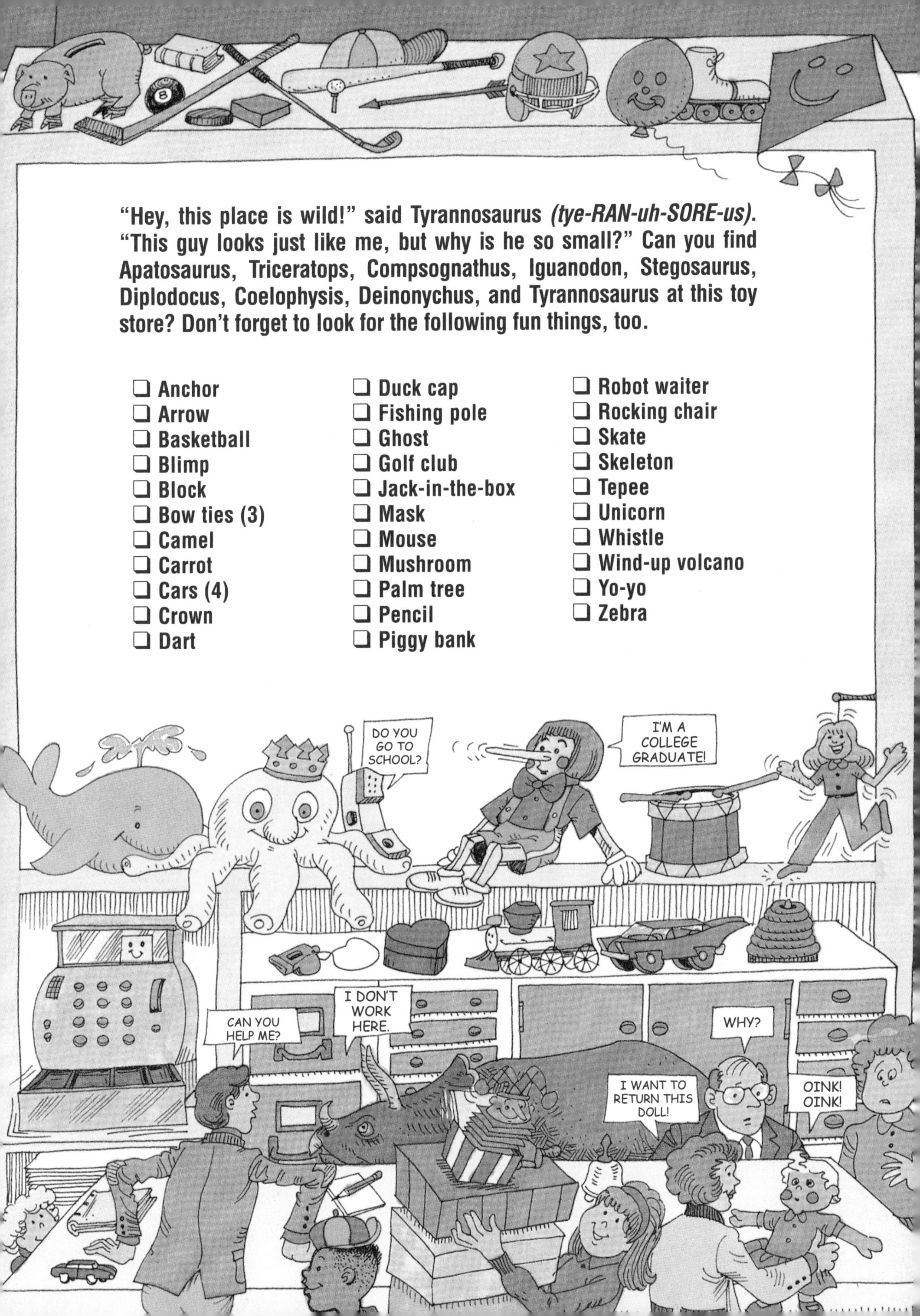

I WANT TO CLIMB A TALL BUILDING.
I'M THE DOCTOR IN THE HOUSE.
ARE YOU A BALLOON?
I'M A BALLOON DROP-OUT!
GIANT SALE
I HAVE TO CHECK THIS OUT.
MARCH THIS WAY!
I'M READY FOR THE END OF THE PARADE.
COME BACK HERE, SAM!
IS THIS A CLASS-ROOM?
THEY'LL ALL BE HUNGRY!
MOO!

"Oh, wow! What are those things flying in the air?" wondered Ankylosaurus *(an-KYE-low-SORE-us)*. Can you find Apatosaurus, Compsognathus, Triceratops, Iguanodon, Stegosaurus, Diplodocus, Coelophysis, Deinonychus, Tyrannosaurus, and Ankylosaurus at this big-balloon parade? Don't forget to look for the following fun things, too.

- ❑ Birds (2)
- ❑ Broom
- ❑ Candy cane
- ❑ Clown
- ❑ Coffeepot
- ❑ Cooking pot
- ❑ Cow
- ❑ Deflated balloon
- ❑ Dummy mummy
- ❑ Fire hydrant
- ❑ Fish
- ❑ Giant
- ❑ Hammer
- ❑ Happy stars (5)
- ❑ Humpty Dumpty
- ❑ Ice skates (2 pairs)
- ❑ King Kong
- ❑ Kite
- ❑ Knight
- ❑ Lion
- ❑ Mouse
- ❑ Paintbrush
- ❑ Penguin
- ❑ Pirate
- ❑ Rabbits (2)
- ❑ Scarecrow
- ❑ Skier
- ❑ Sore feet
- ❑ Three Little Pigs
- ❑ Turtles (2)
- ❑ Unicyclist

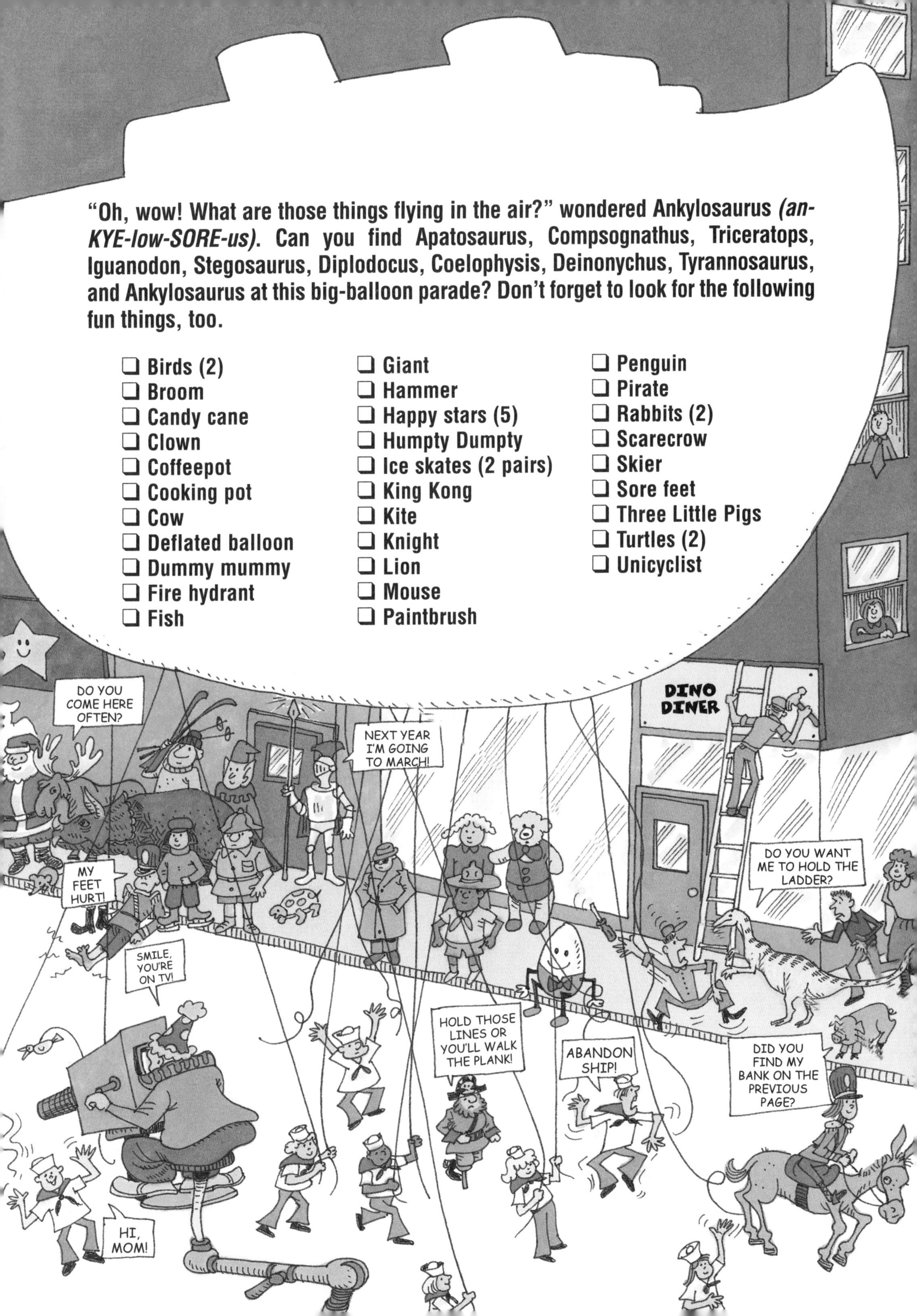

"Here we are, back in this weird cave," said Apatosaurus. "It's really wacky around here. I'm ready to go home, back to prehistoric times." The dinosaurs looked at one another. "But how?" they asked. Before Apatosaurus could answer, the cave shook. Once again the dino friends were traveling through time. But did they make it home—or land in another time and place?

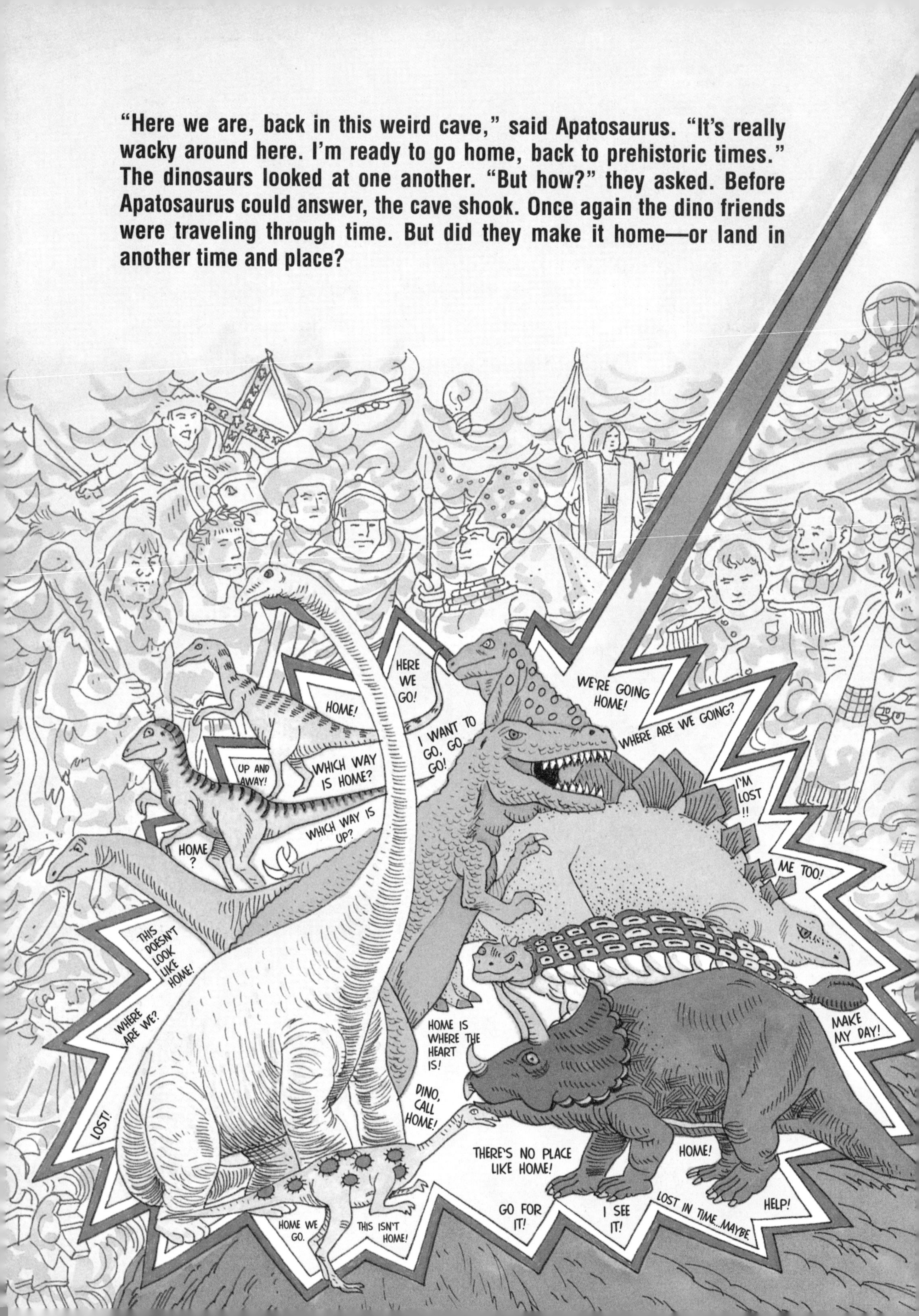

WHERE ARE THEY?

FIND FREDDIE & LISA IN THE HAUNTED HOUSE
CREEPY CASTLE
FIND FRANKIE & HIS MONSTER FRIENDS
MONSTER MADNESS

Spook yourself silly in the haunted house looking for Freddie and Lisa.

Search through the creepy castle.

Find Frankie and his monster friends.

Experience monster madness!

FIND FREDDIE & LISA

IN THE

HAUNTED HOUSE

Freddie and Lisa have discovered a house that is unlike any other—a haunted house!

FIND FREDDIE & LISA AT THE HAUNTED HOUSE, AND THESE FUN ITEMS:

- ☒ Apples (2)
- ☒ Baseball cap
- ☒ Bones (3)
- ☒ Box
- ☒ Burned-out candle
- ☒ Clothespin
- ☒ Coffeepot
- ☒ Crown
- ☒ Dog
- ☒ Duck
- ☒ Eyeglasses
- ☒ Faucet
- ☒ Fish tank
- ☒ Ghosts (3)
- ☒ Hammer
- ☒ Heart
- ☒ Kite
- ☒ Lips
- ☒ Mouse
- ☒ Owl
- ☒ Paint bucket
- ☒ Peanut
- ☒ Pencils (2)
- ☒ Piggy bank
- ☒ Saw
- ☒ Sock
- ☒ Submarine
- ☒ Truck
- ☒ Umbrella

WHOOOOOOO!
WE'RE GOING TO HAVE COMPANY!
I LOVE GUESTS!
THEY KEEP ME IN THE ATTIC!
NO FISHING ALLOWED!
DID YOU SEE ME?
I'M GOING OUT.
ULP!
PERK! PERK! PERK!
WHERE'S THE LAUNDRY?
COME ON IN!!
IT'S RAINING!
I'M YOUR MUMMY!
STEP ASIDE! I'M NOT GOING IN THERE!
ME TOO!
I DON'T KNOW?

Should they go in?
Should they stay in?
What do you think they should do?

FIND FREDDIE & LISA BEFORE THEY DECIDE, AND THESE FUN ITEMS:

- Birds (2)
- Blimps (2)
- Bowling ball
- Broom
- Camel
- Candle
- Chef's hat
- Feather
- Flower
- Football
- Giraffe
- Jester
- King
- Laundry
- Lost boot
- Mustache
- Napoleon
- Painted egg
- Rabbit
- Red wagon
- Sailboat
- Short pants
- Skull
- Sled
- Slide
- Star
- Top hats (2)
- Trash can
- Umbrella

GO...
GO!
I CAN'T GO!
DON'T GO IN THE HOUSE LATER...GO NOW!
OH, GO / AHEAD!
DO I GO?
DO NOT GO...
I'M STAYING HERE!
I'M WAITING FOR WINTER.
GO!
ME TOO!
ONWARD!
IF WE DON'T GO IN... THE BOOK ENDS HERE!!
DON'T GO!
?
THAT'S BETTER!
KICK ME!
THEN, LET'S GO IN!
WHERE?
SOMETHING TELLS ME I SHOULDN'T GO!
I'M LOST!
GET ME OUT OF HERE!
LET'S GO!
NO!
DID SOMEONE SAY, "PIZZA?"
WHAT DOES IT SAY?
I WANT TO GO!
I'M GOING!
LOST
WHO ORDERED PIZZA?
WAIT FOR ME!
I'M GOING TO WIN THE BEST COSTUME CONTEST.
?
Y-GO?
CAN I GO?
STOP DON'T GO OH, GO AHEAD!
?
?
?
?

Ready, set, go! Everyone runs toward the door of the haunted house, but only two enter it!

FIND FREDDIE & LISA AS THEY MEET THE MONSTERS, AND THESE FUN ITEMS:

- ❑ Apple
- ❑ Arrow
- ❑ Bag
- ❑ Balloon
- ❑ Banana peel
- ❑ Baseball cap
- ❑ Bone
- ❑ Boot
- ❑ Broken heart
- ❑ Broom
- ❑ Cake
- ❑ Candles (5)
- ❑ Crystal ball
- ❑ Fish
- ❑ Genie
- ❑ Ghosts (2)
- ❑ Ice-cream cone
- ❑ Lightning
- ❑ Necktie
- ❑ Owl
- ❑ Piano
- ❑ Skulls (5)
- ❑ Snake
- ❑ Spoon
- ❑ Tombstone

GLAD TO MEET YOU!
HI, GUY!
WHO! WHO'S THERE?
THEY DON'T SCARE ME!!!
I'LL JUST WAIT HERE.
OOPS!
HOWDY.
YOU'RE CUTE.
WHERE DID I PUT IT THIS TIME?
NO EXIT
HOW POLITE! THEY CLOSED THE DOOR BEHIND THEM!
HOW LONG WILL THEY STAY?
SLAM!

Ms. Witch makes gross snacks. Her specialty is the "Everything Goes" sandwich!

FIND FREDDIE & LISA AT SNACK TIME, AND THESE FUN ITEMS:

- ❑ Accordion
- ❑ Apple
- ❑ Baseball
- ❑ Blackbird
- ❑ Bone
- ❑ Candle
- ❑ Checkerboard
- ❑ Drill
- ❑ Earring
- ❑ Fish (2)
- ❑ Flower
- ❑ Fork
- ❑ Frying pan
- ❑ Grapes
- ❑ Green cup
- ❑ Heart
- ❑ Helmet
- ❑ Ice-cream cone
- ❑ Ladle
- ❑ Neckties (2)
- ❑ Oilcan
- ❑ Orange
- ❑ Palm tree
- ❑ Pear
- ❑ Rolling pin
- ❑ Saw
- ❑ Sock
- ❑ Stool
- ❑ Toaster
- ❑ Wooden spoon

I'M A SLICE OF PICKLE...
...AND YOU'RE NOT!
I'M NOT HAPPY UP HERE!
HERE YOU ARE, OXCAR. I HOPE YOU LIKE THIS SNACK.
OH, THANK YOU SO MUCH, MS. WITCH!
I CAN'T BELIEVE HE CAN EAT THE WHOLE THING!
IT MAKES ME HUNGRY!
A WORLD RECORD SNACK!
DID SHE LEAVE ANYTHING OUT OF THAT SNACK?
ME!

Freddie and Lisa begin to explore the haunted house. A wrong turn, and down they tumble!

FIND FREDDIE & LISA IN THE DUNGEON, AND THESE FUN ITEMS:

- ❑ Airplane
- ❑ Balloon
- ❑ Banana peel
- ❑ Bowling ball
- ❑ Broken egg
- ❑ Broom
- ❑ Candy cane
- ❑ Corn
- ❑ Cupcake
- ❑ Doctor
- ❑ Drum
- ❑ Fire hydrant
- ❑ Flowerpot
- ❑ Flying bat
- ❑ Football
- ❑ Hot dog
- ❑ Ice-cream cone
- ❑ Ice-cream pop
- ❑ Mummies (3)
- ❑ Piggy bank
- ❑ Rabbit
- ❑ Roller skates
- ❑ Scarecrow
- ❑ Shark
- ❑ Skateboard
- ❑ Skulls (2)
- ❑ Skunk
- ❑ Top hat
- ❑ Umbrellas (2)
- ❑ Wagon

WHO ORDERED A CASE OF JITTERS?
HI, GUYS!
SICK!
I MUST PULL MYSELF TOGETHER!
SHUT THAT LIGHT!
OOPS!
DUNGEON TOURS
THIS PLACE IS GETTING TOO CROWDED!
QUIET.
HE'S GOT US!
YOU'RE NEW HERE!
IT'S VERY ROOMY HERE!
WHERE'S MY WITCH?
IT'S A NICE PLACE TO VISIT, BUT I'M NOT LIVING HERE!!
PLAY YOUR CARDS RIGHT LAD, AND SOME DAY THIS WILL ALL BE YOURS!
I'M SCARED.
I SEE YOU!
13
DO NOT DISTURB (COUNT DRACULA)
FOR RENT
IT'S ALMOST HATCHED!
R.I.P.
GET OFF ME, KID!
VERY, VERY QUICK SAND!
GO FOR IT!
I'M RUNNING IN THE RAT RACE!
GIVE ME, A PENNY!
WRONG WAY

Next to the dungeon are the wildest lanes in town. It's a great place to do anything—but bowl!

FIND FREDDIE & LISA AT THE GHOSTLY BOWLING ALLEY, AND THESE FUN ITEMS:

- ❑ Arrow
- ❑ Balloon
- ❑ Bird
- ❑ Bodiless head
- ❑ Broken ball
- ❑ Broom
- ❑ Cactus
- ❑ Candles (2)
- ❑ Carrot
- ❑ Dog
- ❑ Earphones
- ❑ Flower
- ❑ Hamburger
- ❑ Hot dog
- ❑ Mouse
- ❑ Mummy
- ❑ Mummy's ball
- ❑ Orange
- ❑ Pear
- ❑ Periscope
- ❑ Robot
- ❑ Sailboat
- ❑ Snowman
- ❑ Spring
- ❑ Sunglasses (2 pairs)
- ❑ Sword
- ❑ Tennis racket
- ❑ Tombstone
- ❑ Yo-yo

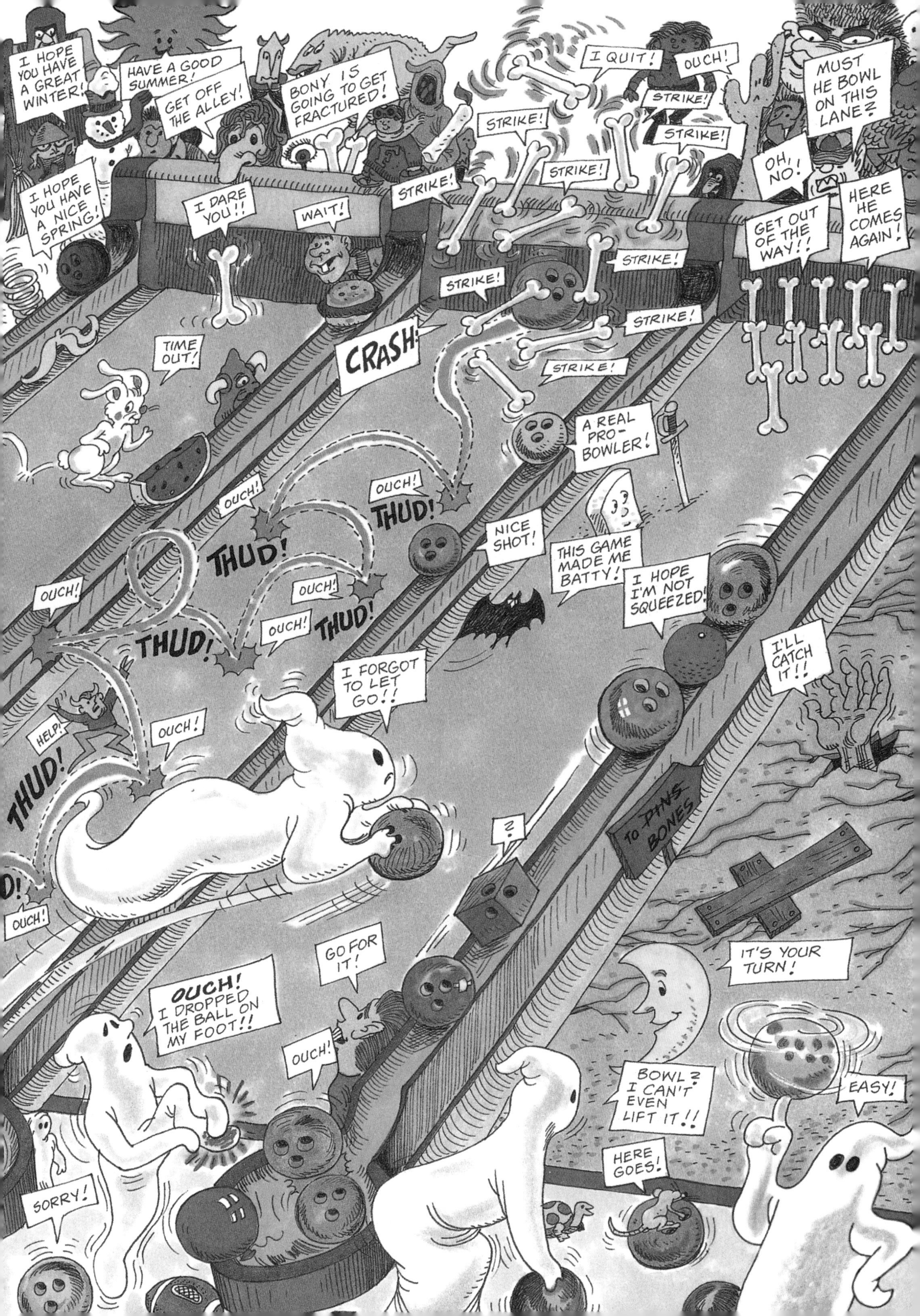

I HOPE YOU HAVE A GREAT WINTER!
HAVE A GOOD SUMMER!
GET OFF THE ALLEY!
BONY IS GOING TO GET FRACTURED!
I QUIT!
OUCH!
STRIKE!
STRIKE!
MUST HE BOWL ON THIS LANE?
STRIKE!
STRIKE!
STRIKE!
I HOPE YOU HAVE A NICE SPRING!
I DARE YOU!!
WAIT!
OH, NO!
HERE HE COMES AGAIN!
GET OUT OF THE WAY!!
STRIKE!
STRIKE!
STRIKE!
STRIKE!
CRASH!
TIME OUT!
A REAL PRO-BOWLER!
OUCH!
OUCH!
THUD!
THUD!
NICE SHOT!
THIS GAME MADE ME BATTY!
I HOPE I'M NOT SQUEEZED!
OUCH!
OUCH!
THUD!
OUCH!
THUD!
OUCH!
I FORGOT TO LET GO!!
I'LL CATCH IT!!
HELP!
OUCH!
THUD!
?
To PINS BONES
D!
OUCH!
GO FOR IT!
IT'S YOUR TURN!
OUCH! I DROPPED THE BALL ON MY FOOT!!
OUCH!
BOWL? I CAN'T EVEN LIFT IT!!
EASY!
HERE GOES!
SORRY!

Dr. Frankenstein has lots of patients who need lots of patience.

FIND FREDDIE & LISA IN DR. FRANKENSTEIN'S LABORATORY, AND THESE FUN ITEMS:

- ☒ Black cat
- ☐ Book
- ☐ Bride
- ☐ Bunny fiend
- ☐ Candle
- ☐ Cheese
- ☐ Dog
- ☐ Dracula
- ☐ Duck
- ☐ Feather
- ☐ Greeting card
- ☐ Ice-cream pop
- ☐ Invisible person
- ☐ Paintbrush
- ☐ Paint bucket
- ☐ Pickax
- ☐ Roller skates
- ☐ Sailor fiend
- ☐ Saw
- ☐ Screwdriver
- ☐ Shovel
- ☐ Skull
- ☐ Suspenders
- ☐ Three-legged thing
- ☐ Toy block
- ☐ Tulip
- ☐ TV set
- ☐ Two-headed thing
- ☐ Watch

THIS IS DUMB!
I'M LATE!
I'M NOT!
I HAVE A SORE THROAT.
I'M ON A DIET.
I NEED A NEW JOB!
THE DOCTOR IS IN
I THINK SOMETHING IS WRONG.
I'M STUCK!
I HAVE AN APPOINTMENT.
I'M NEXT!
NO! I'M NEXT!
A BEAUTIFUL BRIDE!
IS MY HUSBAND-TO-BE READY?
I'VE BEEN WAITING SINCE MIDNIGHT!
ME TOO!
IT'S HOT HERE.
I'VE BEEN WAITING THE LONGEST!
I GOT THIS FROM A SECOND-HAND STORE!
DID YOU KNOW THAT IGOR SNORES?
OH, NO!! NOT THAT!
EVEN WHEN HE'S AWAKE.
HOW CAN YOU PROVE THAT, INVISIBLE PERSON?
I GOT THIS FROM A RETAIL SHOP!
I'M COMING, I'M COMING! (WHAT A GROUCH!)
ABNORMAL SPINACH
IS IT MY TURN YET?
I HAVE A TOOTHACHE!
THIS DOCTOR IS A QUACK!
YOU DROPPED SOMETHING!
YOU CAN COUNT ON ME!
VERY FUNNY LINE, COUNT DRACULA!
HE CAN'T COUNT BEYOND THE FINGERS ON HIS HANDS!
OH, UP TO 13!
NORMAL SPINACH

After dinner, Freddie and Lisa explore a room upstairs. There they find someone who *really* knows how to save!

FIND FREDDIE & LISA IN DRACULA'S ATTIC, AND THESE FUN ITEMS:

- ❑ Boomerang
- ❑ Broom
- ❑ Candy cane
- ❑ Chef's hat
- ❑ Clocks (2)
- ❑ Cracked mirror
- ❑ Fire hydrant
- ❑ Garden hose
- ❑ Golf club
- ❑ Ice-cream cone
- ❑ Key
- ❑ Mouse
- ❑ Necklace
- ❑ Oar
- ❑ Paint bucket
- ❑ Paper airplane
- ❑ Pencil
- ❑ Pyramid
- ❑ Saw
- ❑ Skateboard
- ❑ Skulls (4)
- ❑ Slice of pizza
- ❑ Spray can
- ❑ Straw
- ❑ String of pearls
- ❑ Stuffed panda
- ❑ Telephone booth
- ❑ Viking helmet
- ❑ Yarn

DON'T READ THIS NOTICE
WHAT'S FOR LUNCH?
BOOM!
ONE WAY
YOU HAVE THREE WISHES.
THIS PLACE IS A MESS.
I'M NOT COMING OUT!!
DRACULA'S MOTTO: NEVER THROW ANYTHING AWAY!
WHERE'S MY HAT?
I'M A DUST BUNNY, AND I'M LEAVING!
I'M GOING HOME!
THIS SIDE UP
TRANSYLVANIA OR BUST!
I WAS USED ONLY ON SATURDAY NIGHTS!
FOR SALE!
DON'T GET UP, COUNT DRACULA. I'M HERE TO CLEAN!!!
BUT, I DON'T DO WINDOWS!
WHERE'S THE KEY?
WHICH SIDE UP?

The monsters walk very carefully when they visit *this* room!

FIND FREDDIE & LISA IN THE COBWEB ROOM, AND THESE FUN ITEMS:

- ❑ Baby carriage
- ❑ Binoculars
- ❑ Bow tie
- ❑ Boxing glove
- ❑ Broom
- ❑ Cup
- ❑ Dog
- ❑ Duck
- ❑ Earring
- ❑ Electric plug
- ❑ Fish
- ❑ Flower
- ❑ Football helmet
- ❑ Fork
- ❑ Ghosts (2)
- ❑ Hammer
- ❑ Heart
- ❑ Key
- ❑ Lock
- ❑ Moon face
- ❑ Mummy
- ❑ Old-fashioned radio
- ❑ Pencil
- ❑ Ring
- ❑ Robot
- ❑ Screwdriver
- ❑ Ship
- ❑ Skull
- ❑ Top hat
- ❑ Turtles (2)
- ❑ Wagon

NICE PLACE TO VISIT!
I'M EMPTY!
I BELONG TO FRANKENSTEIN'S MONSTER.
I'M THE HEART OF THIS WEB!
I'VE BEEN VERY BUSY!
CLEAN YOUR ROOM!

Playtime for monsters!

FIND FREDDIE & LISA IN THE MONSTERS' PLAYROOM, AND THESE FUN ITEMS:

- ❑ Artist
- ❑ Balloon
- ❑ Banana peel
- ❑ Barbell
- ❑ Birds (2)
- ❑ Blackboard
- ❑ Crayons (5)
- ❑ Donkey
- ❑ Fish
- ❑ Football
- ❑ Haunted house
- ❑ Hole in the head
- ❑ Hood
- ❑ Ice skate
- ❑ Jack-o'-lanterns (4)
- ❑ Joke book
- ❑ Juggler
- ❑ Mask
- ❑ Monster puppet
- ❑ Mummy doll
- ❑ Musician
- ❑ Nail
- ❑ Pail
- ❑ Pogo stick
- ❑ Rubber ducky
- ❑ Sailboat
- ❑ Snake
- ❑ Telephone
- ❑ Tricycle
- ❑ Turtle
- ❑ Wind-up monster

OH, GIVE ME A HOME, WHERE MONSTERS DO ROAM.
I LIKE TO SWING.
I'M GOING TO THE BULL'S EYE.
UGH! WHERE DID YOU GET SUCH A HORRIBLE MASK ???
TRICK OR TRICK?
SHE'S A COPY CAT!!
POLLUTED WATER
WHO'S WINNING?
REFEREE!
THIS IS PERFECT.
NO WAY!
JUST RIGHT!
THIS IS MY TOY CHEST AND YOU CAN'T PLAY WITH IT!!
GONE FROM FISHING
I WANT TO PLAY TOO!
I'M NOT GOING IN THERE!
THIS IS MY MUMMY DOLL!
HORROR U
BOO!
GET ME OUT OF HERE!
MUMMY!
HERE I COME!
HE'S GOT MY TAIL!
BEAUTIFUL DRAWING!
NICE.
BOING!
NICE.
GO, JACK, GO!
WHERE'S THE WATER?
MOTHER
DRAW ME!
GO, JACK, GO!
THE BEST WAY TO TALK TO KING KONG IS BY LONG DISTANCE.
JOKE BOOK

It is time for Freddie and Lisa to go. The friendly monsters hope their new friends will return soon.

FIND FREDDIE & LISA LEAVING THE HAUNTED HOUSE, AND THESE FUN ITEMS:

- ❑ Apple
- ❑ Arrow
- ❑ Balloon
- ❑ Birds (2)
- ❑ Box
- ❑ Broken heart
- ❑ Brooms (2)
- ❑ Candles (2)
- ❑ Clock
- ❑ Crown
- ❑ Dog
- ❑ Duck
- ❑ Envelope
- ❑ Flower
- ❑ Ice skates
- ❑ Key
- ❑ Ladder
- ❑ Lamp
- ❑ Moon face
- ❑ Mouse
- ❑ Painted egg
- ❑ Periscope
- ❑ Rabbit
- ❑ Roller skates
- ❑ Shovel
- ❑ Skull
- ❑ TV camera
- ❑ Umbrella

THIS HOUSE IS ON A DEAD-END STREET!
COME FLY WITH ME, FREDDIE AND LISA!
SMILE!
DID THEY LEAVE YET?
BACK DOOR
THEY'RE OUT OF THE HAUNTED HOUSE!
HOW WAS IT?
I'M SUPER KID.
WE HAD A LOT OF FUN!
IT'S NOT RAINING!
I'M STUCK!
I'M A PANE!
GOOD-BYE, FREDDIE AND LISA!
I WISH I HAD GONE INSIDE, TOO!
WAIT UNTIL NEXT YEAR.
YIPE!
I'M STAYING IN HERE!
DON'T FORGET US!
HE'S CUTE!
I CHANGED MY MIND...I'M STAYING OUT!
I FEEL A DRAFT.
I HOPE THEY DON'T SEE ME!
ARE THEY FLYING SOUTH FOR THE WINTER?
DO COME AGAIN.
THEY ARE LEAVING US?
GOOD LUCK!
NICE TO HAVE MET YOU.
DON'T FORGET TO WRITE!
CAPTAIN, I THINK WE'RE LOST!
WE HAD A BLAST!
AHOY!
ALOHA.

Freddie and Lisa are here
with a few of their playmates:

Bunny Honey
Donald
Frankie
Hector
Laura
Sam
Santa
Santa's helpers: Fee, Fi, Fo, and Fun
Susie

MONSTER MADNESS

There once was an old house, in an old part of town, that was discovered by two children. They wanted to go inside, but first they had to find the following hidden pictures. Can you help them?
❑ Banana
❑ Bone
❑ Book
❑ Boot
❑ Bottle
❑ Broom
❑ Carrot
❑ Elephant
❑ Envelope
❑ Fish
❑ Flower
❑ Hairbrush
❑ Hammer
❑ Heart
❑ Hockey stick
❑ Horseshoe
❑ Hot dog
❑ Lost wallet
❑ Owl
❑ Palm tree
❑ Rabbit
❑ Sailboat
❑ Saw
❑ Screwdriver
❑ Skull
❑ Snake
❑ Star
❑ Toothbrush
❑ Zipper
WELCOME TO ANCIENT ACRES
WE FOUND IT! LET'S GO INSIDE!
NOT FOR SALE

13
WE DARE YOU!

In the old house was an old trunk, which the children opened with an old key. Out of the trunk came many strange things, including these hidden objects:

- ☐ Arrow
- ☐ Balloon
- ☐ Bearded man
- ☐ Carrot
- ☐ Chicken
- ☐ Fish
- ☐ Giraffe
- ☐ Horse
- ☐ Kite
- ☐ Moon face
- ☐ Mouse
- ☐ Snowman
- ☐ Tepee
- ☐ Tombstone
- ☐ Turtle
- ☐ Unicorn

HELLO!
I GOT MY WISH!
WHAT YEAR IS IT?
LET'S GO FOR A WALK.
WHAT CENTURY IS IT?
THANKS FOR LETTING US OUT!
IT'S GOOD TO GET OUT!
OH-OH!!

WAIT FOR US!
I'M YOUR VERY OWN MUMMY!
LET ME PLAY FOR YOU!
SLOW DOWN!
Did you ever see such a sight in your life? It's not three blind mice—it's monsters! Monsters can be found everywhere, along with the following hidden pictures. Can you find them all?
Arrow
Automobile
Candle
Candy canes (2)
Clothespin
Comb
Drum
Evergreen tree
Fish
Flower
Football
Hairbrush
Hot dog
Kangaroo
Key
Locket
Mouse
Pen
Pencil
Skateboard
Sock
Tent
Umbrella

FOR RENT
THESE ARE GOOFY MONSTERS!
LET'S FIND MORE!!

COME ON IN!
I WANT TO SEE THE PICTURES.
NEWSPAPER
OLD NEWS

In another room in the old house, the two kids found an ancient family album. Whose pictures do you think were inside? Before you can open it, you must find the following objects.
Arrow
Banana
Bear
Cactus
Cane
Cat
Deer
Fork
Frog
Giraffe
Heart
Ice-cream cone
Monkey
Mouse
Owl
Pencil
Pig
Rabbit
Ring
Rooster
Saw
Skull
Snake
Star

Wow! What a surprise! It is a photo album full of monsters! On the first page, there is a picture of young Frankenstein on his first date. Do you know which monster is on the next page? Before you look, find the following hidden objects:
❑ Airplane
❑ Automobile
❑ Butterfly
❑ Camera
❑ Candle
❑ Cup
❑ Drum
❑ Eyeglasses
❑ Fish
❑ Hearts (4)
❑ House
❑ Kite
❑ Light bulb
❑ Owl
❑ Pencil
❑ Ring
❑ Rocket
❑ Sailboat
❑ Snake
❑ Surfboard
❑ Sword
❑ Tent
❑ Toothpaste
❑ Tree
❑ Turtle
❑ Umbrella
❑ Whistle

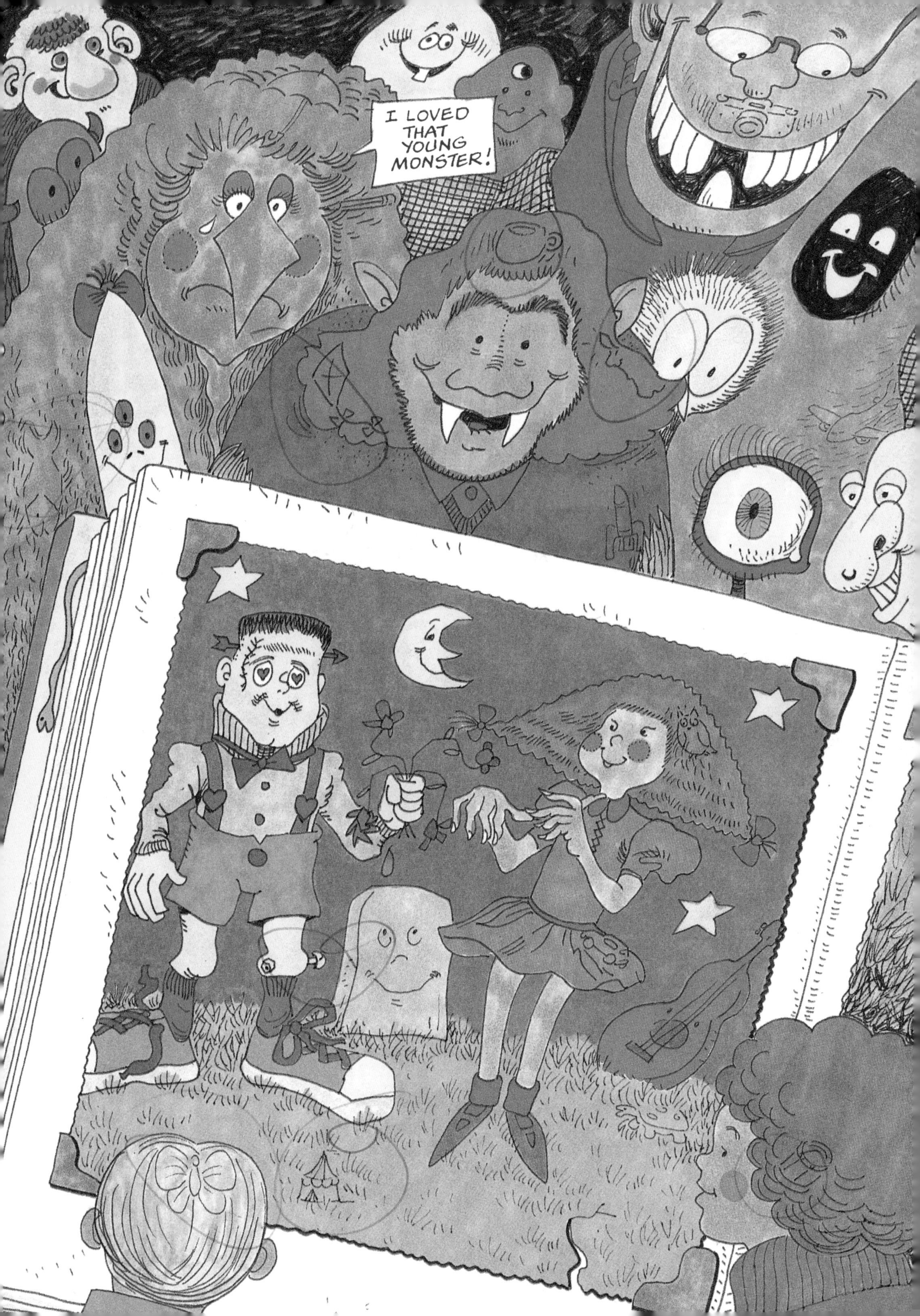
I LOVED THAT YOUNG MONSTER!

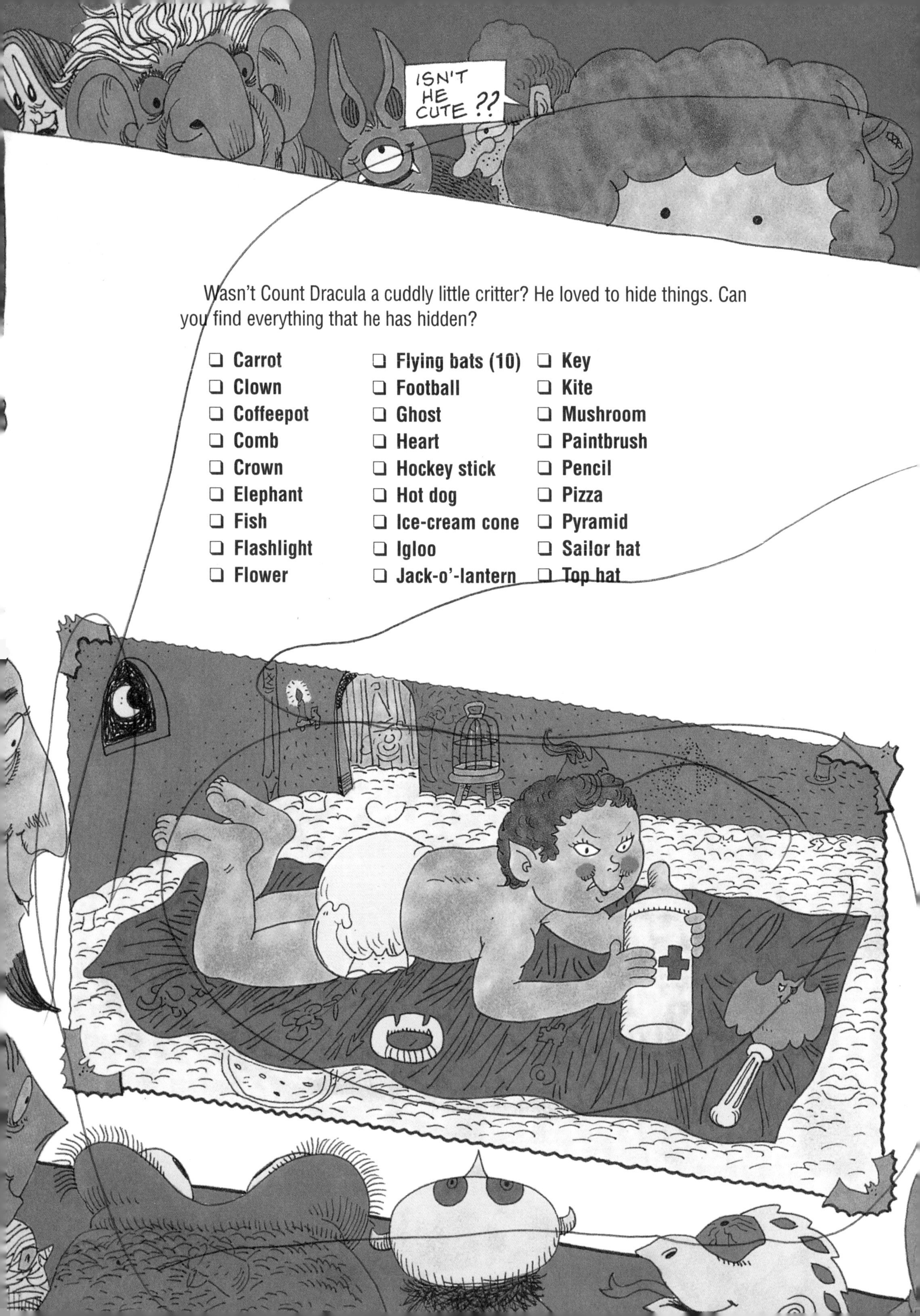

Wasn't Count Dracula a cuddly little critter? He loved to hide things. Can you find everything that he has hidden?

- ❑ **Carrot**
- ❑ **Clown**
- ❑ **Coffeepot**
- ❑ **Comb**
- ❑ **Crown**
- ❑ **Elephant**
- ❑ **Fish**
- ❑ **Flashlight**
- ❑ **Flower**
- ❑ **Flying bats (10)**
- ❑ **Football**
- ❑ **Ghost**
- ❑ **Heart**
- ❑ **Hockey stick**
- ❑ **Hot dog**
- ❑ **Ice-cream cone**
- ❑ **Igloo**
- ❑ **Jack-o'-lantern**
- ❑ **Key**
- ❑ **Kite**
- ❑ **Mushroom**
- ❑ **Paintbrush**
- ❑ **Pencil**
- ❑ **Pizza**
- ❑ **Pyramid**
- ❑ **Sailor hat**
- ❑ **Top hat**

I DELIVER PAPERS, TOO.

This is the largest picture in the monster family album. It is the abominable snow kid building snow monsters. He has also thrown in some hidden pictures. Look closely to find them all.

- ❑ **Alligator**
- ❑ **Banana**
- ❑ **Bow tie**
- ❑ **Cactus**
- ❑ **Can**
- ❑ **Candle**
- ❑ **Cheese**
- ❑ **Chef's hat**
- ❑ **Cowboy hat**
- ❑ **Duck**
- ❑ **Fish**
- ❑ **Ghost**
- ❑ **Heart**
- ❑ **Hot dog**
- ❑ **Ice-cream cone**
- ❑ **Ice skate**
- ❑ **Ladder**
- ❑ **Lamp**
- ❑ **Lion**
- ❑ **Mouse**
- ❑ **Paintbrush**
- ❑ **Picture frame**
- ❑ **Pie**
- ❑ **Pig**
- ❑ **Pirate**
- ❑ **Shoe**
- ❑ **Shovel**
- ❑ **Top hat**
- ❑ **Umbrella**
- ❑ **Watering can**

Here is the mummy, showing off his childhood pictures. You sure can get wrapped up in them! You also can get wrapped up in looking for the following hidden objects.

- ❑ **Apple**
- ❑ **Arrow**
- ❑ **Artist**
- ❑ **Bird**
- ❑ **Blimp**
- ❑ **Bone**
- ❑ **Book**
- ❑ **Cupcake**
- ❑ **Drum**
- ❑ **Fish**
- ❑ **Football**
- ❑ **Ghost**
- ❑ **Golf club**
- ❑ **Hammer**
- ❑ **Kangaroo**
- ❑ **Kite**
- ❑ **Owl**
- ❑ **Pinocchio**
- ❑ **Sailor hat**
- ❑ **Saw**
- ❑ **Scarecrow**
- ❑ **Wagon**

CRYPT-U
MY OWN ROOM
MY FIRST SAND-BOX

These are really terrific pictures—the best in the album! They are, of course, pictures of the invisible man throughout the years. Try to find the following objects:

- ❑ **Banana**
- ❑ **Basket**
- ❑ **Bone**
- ❑ **Carrot**
- ❑ **Cheese**
- ❑ **Evergreen tree**
- ❑ **Fire hydrant**
- ❑ **Football**
- ❑ **Graduation cap**
- ❑ **Guitar**
- ❑ **Hamburger**
- ❑ **Heart**
- ❑ **Hot dog**
- ❑ **Ice-cream soda**
- ❑ **Light bulb**
- ❑ **Mouse**
- ❑ **Pear**
- ❑ **Pencil**
- ❑ **Rose**
- ❑ **Screwdriver**
- ❑ **Shovel**
- ❑ **Snail**
- ❑ **Star**
- ❑ **Tent**
- ❑ **Turtle**
- ❑ **TV set**
- ❑ **Unicorn**

INVISIBLE PAPER

FIRST BIRTHDAY

KID LEAGUE STAR

FIRST DAY OF SCHOOL

SCHOOL FIELD TRIP

SOCCER CHAMP

TALKING TO SANTA

FIRST INVISIBLE MAN ON THE MOON

One picture is too big to fit into the album.
It's so big, it's hiding the following hidden pictures:

- ❑ Balloons (2)
- ❑ Birdhouse
- ❑ Birds (2)
- ❑ Boat
- ❑ Clock
- ❑ Coffeepot
- ❑ Covered wagon
- ❑ Crown
- ❑ Dog
- ❑ Elephant
- ❑ Fish (3)
- ❑ Hearts (2)
- ❑ Horseshoe
- ❑ Jack-o'-lantern
- ❑ Key
- ❑ Kite
- ❑ Mailbox
- ❑ Mermaid
- ❑ Old radio
- ❑ Old sock
- ❑ Old tire
- ❑ Pizza
- ❑ Tepee
- ❑ Worm

The monsters are so happy to have shared their family album, they asked the children to pose with them for a group photograph. Before the picture can be taken, you must find the following objects:

- ❑ Bird's nest
- ❑ Bow tie
- ❑ Boxing glove
- ❑ Butterfly
- ❑ Camel
- ❑ Cow
- ❑ Crayon
- ❑ Dinosaur
- ❑ Eight ball
- ❑ Elephant
- ❑ False teeth
- ❑ Fish
- ❑ Flying bat
- ❑ Football
- ❑ Football helmet
- ❑ Hamburger
- ❑ Hammer
- ❑ Igloo
- ❑ Kite
- ❑ Locomotive
- ❑ Model plane
- ❑ Mouse
- ❑ Musical note
- ❑ Paintbrush
- ❑ Sled
- ❑ Snake
- ❑ Tent
- ❑ Thermometer
- ❑ Top hat
- ❑ Wind-up car

DID YOU ENJOY OUR FAMILY PICTURES?

FIND
FRANKIE
AND HIS
MONSTER
FRIENDS

Early one morning, Frankie has a brilliant idea. He decides to visit some friends he hasn't seen in a long time.

FIND FRANKIE IN HIS NUTTY NEIGHBORHOOD, AND THESE FUN ITEMS:

❑ Book
❑ Bowling ball
❑ Bucket
❑ Candle
❑ Dog
❑ Duck
❑ Fish (3)
❑ Flying bats (3)
❑ Football helmet
❑ Hammer
❑ Heart
❑ Jack-o'-lantern
❑ Moose head
❑ Periscope
❑ Pinocchio
❑ Raincoat
❑ Roller skates
❑ Sailor hat
❑ Scarecrow
❑ Skier
❑ Skull
❑ Star
❑ Tepee
❑ Thermometer
❑ Tulip
❑ Turtle
❑ Watering can
❑ Wreath

DOG CONDO FOR SALE
IS THE SURF UP?
I THOUGHT THERE WAS A FISH IN OUR POOL!
DO NOT DISTURB!
I'M BROKE!
I WONDER WHAT HAPPENED?
I DON'T KNOW!
THEY COULDN'T THINK OF ANY-THING TO PUT THERE!
THIS SECTION OF PAGE IS CLOSED!
WE ARE CLOSED, SO DON'T READ THIS!
I THINK THEY READ IT!!

Frankie first looks for his old, old friend Manny Mummy in a place with lots of sand.

FIND MANNY MUMMY IN THE DRY DESERT, AND THESE FUN ITEMS:

- ❑ Balloons (3)
- ❑ Banana peel
- ❑ Bathtub
- ❑ Birdhouse
- ❑ Brooms (2)
- ❑ Earring
- ❑ Fire hydrant
- ❑ Fish (2)
- ❑ Flower
- ❑ Gas pump
- ❑ Ring
- ❑ Sailor hat
- ❑ Sand castle
- ❑ Sand pail
- ❑ Sled
- ❑ Slingshot
- ❑ Snake
- ❑ Snowman
- ❑ Soccer ball
- ❑ Star
- ❑ Straw
- ❑ Suitcase
- ❑ Surfboard
- ❑ Turtle
- ❑ TV antenna
- ❑ Umbrella
- ❑ Watering can
- ❑ Watermelon slice

WE MADE A WRONG TURN.
I'M NOT GOING TO DROP IN HERE.
DON'T SHIFT!
I WAS ONLY DRIVEN BY A LITTLE OLD LADY ON SUNDAYS.
HA! THE LITTLE OLD LADY-SUNDAY-STORY-AGAIN!
THIS IS THE BEST WAY TO TRAVEL!
WOULD YOU BUY A USED CAMEL FROM HIM?
USED CAMELS
YOU'RE SPEEDING!
I'M NOT MANNY MUMMY! I HAD A SKIING ACCIDENT.
I'M A FISH OUT OF WATER.
THE SURF'S NOT UP!
EXTREMELY QUICK SAND
THIS IS A GIANT SAND TRAP.
HI, FRANKIE! MANNY MUMMY IS OVER HERE!
GRAND OPENING - SAND SALE!
BUSINESS IS BAD.
I WILL GRANT YOU ONE REQUEST!
I HAVEN'T SEEN A CROW IN YEARS!
WHO, ME?
NICE TO SEE YOU, FRANKIE!
DON'T RUB ME THE WRONG WAY.
I'M THE SHIP OF THE DESERT!
I THINK WE'RE LOST.
WHAT'S WATER?
IT'S SO DRY HERE WE DON'T EVEN HAVE POSTAGE "DUE!"
I WROTE A LETTER TO MY FRIEND, SANDY!
HI!
FLORENCE OF ARABIA
DO NOT PICK SAND

Frankie and Manny Mummy set off to find their friend Batty Bat. He lives in a strange place.

FIND BATTY BAT IN TERRIFYING TRANSYLVANIA, AND THESE FUN ITEMS:

- ❑ Alligator
- ❑ Arrows (2)
- ❑ Baker
- ❑ Bones (6)
- ❑ Book
- ❑ Bride and groom
- ❑ Broken heart
- ❑ Broken mirror
- ❑ Candle
- ❑ Dog
- ❑ Fish
- ❑ Flower
- ❑ Football
- ❑ Fortune teller
- ❑ Hair dryer
- ❑ Kite
- ❑ Lion
- ❑ Mouse
- ❑ Nail
- ❑ Octopus
- ❑ Rabbit
- ❑ Scissors
- ❑ Skulls (4)
- ❑ Top hat
- ❑ Training wheels
- ❑ Umbrella
- ❑ Vulture
- ❑ Worm

HEY, BATTY. GOOD TO SEE YOU!
TOMBS -Я- US
GROSS STUFF
CRYPTS MADE WHILE-U-WAIT.
DID YOU DO YOUR HOMEWORK?
13
8
I'M NOT LOOKING FOR SOMEBODY... I'M LOOKING FOR MY BODY.
I'LL BE HOME FOR BREAKFAST.
FRANKIE IS NEAR!
I HEAR THAT FRANKIE'S HERE.
I SEE!
INSTANT MUD!
I'M A SCAREBAT.
I DO MY OWN HAIR!
I DON'T!
I DON'T!
I SHOULD!

Now they are off to find another pal. This one lives in a swamp!

FIND SWAMPY SAM IN THIS MUSHY MARSH, AND THESE FUN ITEMS:

- ☐ Apple
- ☐ Cupcake
- ☐ Drum
- ☐ Football helmet
- ☐ Fork
- ☐ Frog
- ☐ Grand piano
- ☐ Hammer
- ☐ Key
- ☐ Lost boot
- ☐ Lost mitten
- ☐ Medal
- ☐ Moon face
- ☐ Necktie
- ☐ Palm tree
- ☐ Pencil
- ☐ Pizza slice
- ☐ Ring
- ☐ Snake
- ☐ Soccer ball
- ☐ Sock
- ☐ Speaker
- ☐ Spoon
- ☐ Toothbrush
- ☐ Trumpet
- ☐ Umbrellas (2)

WHO?
DON'T WALK RUN
STOP
ABSOLUTELY NO FISHING
YOU HAVE BAD BREATH!
IT WOULD BE GREAT TO BITE YOU ALL!
GREAT TO SEE YOU ALL!

Warren Werewolf is Frankie's next friend to find. He plays baseball with the Dead End Dodgers.

FIND WARREN WEREWOLF AT THE BALLPARK, AND THESE FUN ITEMS:

- ❑ Bicycle horn
- ❑ Bone
- ❑ Cactus
- ❑ Candy cane
- ❑ Carrot
- ❑ Cookie
- ❑ Crown
- ❑ Empty can
- ❑ Eyeglasses (2)
- ❑ Feather
- ❑ Fir tree
- ❑ Flamingo
- ❑ Footprint
- ❑ Frog
- ❑ Heart
- ❑ Horseshoe
- ❑ Humpty Dumpty
- ❑ Kite
- ❑ Lamp
- ❑ Pliers
- ❑ Six-fingered glove
- ❑ Skull
- ❑ Squirrel
- ❑ Tic-tac-toe
- ❑ Witch
- ❑ Worm

I HAVE TO SEE AN ORTHODONTIST!
DOWN WITH UP SIGNS!
I GOT IT!
I WANT TO PLAY!
SEEDED
PUNT!
THEY NEVER HIT IT TO ME!
NOT THIN ICE
STRIKE!
PUMP!
KEEP OFF THE GRASS
Z
I'M LATE!
DON'T STOP
CAN I HAVE THE CRUMBS?
HELP!
NO HUNTING ALLOWED
ONE WAY
TEAM WHIRLPOOL
I DON'T WANT ANYBODY TO KNOW THAT I'M HERE.
YUM!
THEY ONLY PLAY NIGHT GAMES.
GONE

Frankie and his pals go to an old schoolhouse, where their friend Lena Lightning is a student.

FIND LENA LIGHTNING AMONG HER CREEPY CLASSMATES, AND THESE FUN ITEMS:

- ❑ Apple core
- ❑ Bell
- ❑ Bone tree
- ❑ Broken mirror
- ❑ Cactus
- ❑ Candles (3)
- ❑ Crystal ball
- ❑ Egg
- ❑ Firecracker
- ❑ Flashlight
- ❑ Flying bats (3)
- ❑ Fortune teller
- ❑ Hot dog
- ❑ Ice skate
- ❑ Mask
- ❑ Mouse
- ❑ Necktie
- ❑ Owl
- ❑ Pencil
- ❑ Saw
- ❑ Shark fin
- ❑ Skateboard
- ❑ Skunk
- ❑ Snakes (2)
- ❑ Star
- ❑ Vulture
- ❑ Worm

I WISH I WENT TO SCHOOL HERE.
I'M NOT A TREE! I'M A SPACE CREATURE.
OKAY!
DO YOU CATCH KITES?
IS THIS THE PLACE?
SCHOOL ZONE
ENTER AT YOUR OWN RISK
MY NEW CYCLE.
THIS IS A COOL SCHOOL.
MY HEARSE IS WAITING!
I LIKE TO OPEN THIS INDOORS.
OH, NO!
I HOPE THERE'S NO FISHING ALLOWED HERE!
DO NOT BRING ME A STAKE.
DO THEY HAVE A BALL TEAM?
I FLUNKED!
MEOW!
I HAVE HOMEWORK TO DO.
WATCH YOUR STEP!
BRAINS
AM I NEXT?
OOPS!
I'M THE TEACHER'S PET.
I'M MAJORING IN TOMBSTONE CARVING!
I HOPE I DIDN'T FORGET ANYTHING.
DIDN'T YOU SEE THAT YOU WERE GOING TO TRIP?
DO NOT DISTURB
...OR ELSE!

Next, Frankie and his friends set out to visit Greta Ghost, but none of her neighbors has seen her in a while.

FIND FRANKIE AND HIS OTHER FRIENDS AT GRETA'S HAUNTED HOUSE, AND THESE FUN ITEMS:

- ❑ Alligator
- ❑ Arrows (2)
- ❑ Axe
- ❑ Balloons (5)
- ❑ Banana peel
- ❑ Bowling ball
- ❑ Broom
- ❑ Cup
- ❑ Dart
- ❑ Drum
- ❑ Fork
- ❑ Hammer
- ❑ Hatched egg
- ❑ Heart
- ❑ Keys (2)
- ❑ Ring
- ❑ Screwdriver
- ❑ Ski
- ❑ Stool
- ❑ Sword
- ❑ Teapot
- ❑ Tepee
- ❑ Torn sock
- ❑ Turtle
- ❑ Umbrella
- ❑ Wreath

I'M SCARED.
ME, TOO!
WHO?
I WANT TO GO HOME.
I'VE NEVER SEEN ANYTHING SO FRIGHTENING!
LET'S GO!
THIS IS THE PLACE!
THIS WAY!
WELCOME TO MY COSTUME PARTY.
I'M NOT WEARING ONE.
I WANT SOME PEANUTS.
NICE MASK!
SHAKE!
THIS TICKLES.

It is time for Frankie and friends to say good-bye—for now, that is. They have planned to get together soon, and you are invited to join them!

FIND FRANKIE, MANNY MUMMY, BATTY BAT, SWAMPY SAM, WARREN WEREWOLF, LENA LIGHTNING, GRETA GHOST, AND THESE FUN ITEMS:

- ❑ Apple core
- ❑ Arrow
- ❑ Baseball
- ❑ Bone
- ❑ Crayon
- ❑ Flowerpot
- ❑ Frog
- ❑ Heart
- ❑ Kite
- ❑ Owl
- ❑ Turtle
- ❑ Worm

ENTER AT YOUR OWN RISK!
Creepy Castle

Welcome to Creepy Castle, the castle that was never built. One moonless, creepy night it just appeared! Before you enter, find the following things hidden in this picture.
❑ Airplane
❑ Anchor
❑ Axe
❑ Bottle
❑ Broom
❑ Chair
❑ Clown's face
❑ Cup
❑ Duck
❑ Fire hydrant
❑ Fish
❑ Football
❑ Hammer
❑ Heart
❑ Hockey stick
❑ Key
❑ Paintbrush
❑ Pencil
❑ Ring
❑ Sailboat
GO AHEAD IN!!
SHOULD WE, OR SHOULDN'T WE?
I'LL GO IF YOU GO!!

WELCOME?

So you have decided to enter! Join our fearless friends, who have come to explore Creepy Castle, too. Waiting for them at the bottom of a long staircase is a fire-breathing dragon! Can you see these hidden objects?
Apple
Arrow
Balloon
Bone
Book
Cat
Comb
Donkey's head
Envelope
Fire hydrant
Fish
Fork
Guitar
Heart
Jack-o'-lantern
Magnifying glass
Medal
Paintbrush
Spear
Sword
Tricycle
Turtle
I'M GLAD IT'S ONLY YOU TWO AND NOT THE DRAGON SLAYER!
WOW!
FOR RENT

Racing through a partly open curtain, our friends enter the room of a famous monster star, who has hidden all kinds of things. Can you find them?
Automobile
Axe
Basket
Bird
Bone
Candle
Cups (2)
Elephant
Fish
Flower
Flying bat
Guitar
Hammer
Hearts (2)
Igloo
Kangaroo
Mermaid
Mitten
Moon face
Mouse
Party hat
Pencil
Rabbit
Star
Toothbrush
Tugboat
Whale
WHY DID YOU STOP?
OH, NO!

OH! YOU FRIGHTENED ME!
MUMMY
KNIGHT DAY
PRINCE PRINCE
SIR LOIN
KING SIZE
QUEEN BEE

Now here is a weird sight—a headless knight! Could he be related to the Headless Horseman of Sleepy Hollow?

Before going on, find these hidden pictures.

- **Baseball bat**
- **Book**
- **Bottle**
- **Cow's head**
- **Cupcake**
- **Duck**
- **Eagle's head**
- **Ear of corn**
- **Envelope**
- **Feather**
- **Frog**
- **Ghost**
- **Hot dog**
- **Key**
- **Paper clip**
- **Pea pod**
- **Saw**
- **Shoe**
- **Toothbrush**
- **Turtle**
- **Umbrella**
- **Wheelbarrow**

I THOUGHT HE WEIGHED LESS TODAY.

LOOK AT THIS!!
THE HOODED WARRIOR IS BEING KNIGHTED BY THE KING!

What lurks beneath this new knight's hood? Is he a handsome hero or another creepy creature? Before you turn the page to find out, look for the following hidden pictures.

- Arrow
- Astronaut
- Banana
- Cactus
- Carrot
- Crab
- Electric guitar
- Fish
- Heart
- Helicopter
- Hot dog
- Ice-cream cone
- Invisible knight
- Key
- Kite
- Parachute
- Pelican
- Rocket
- Sailboat
- Skis
- Teapot
- Toothbrush
- Truck
- Turtle

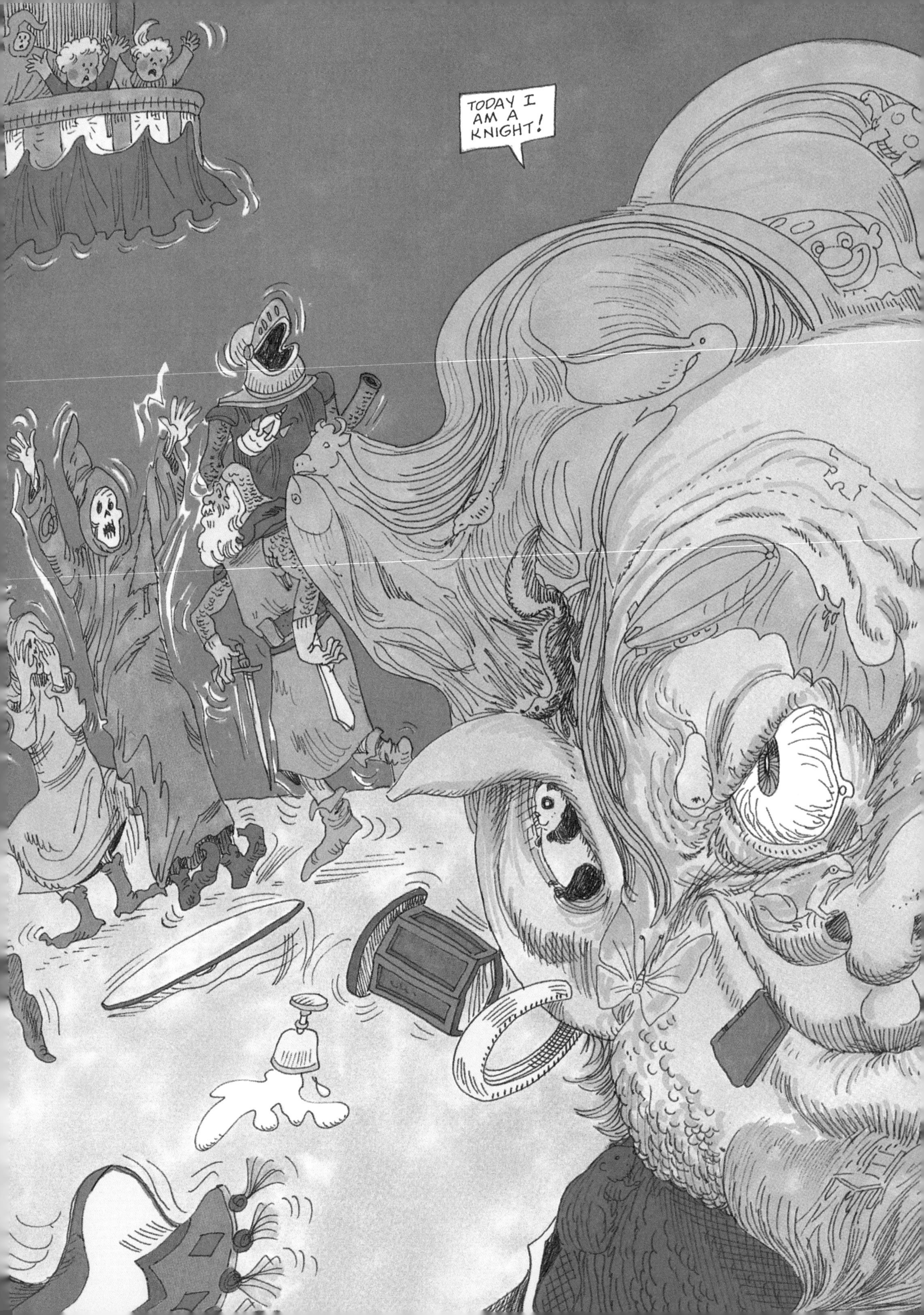
TODAY I AM A KNIGHT!

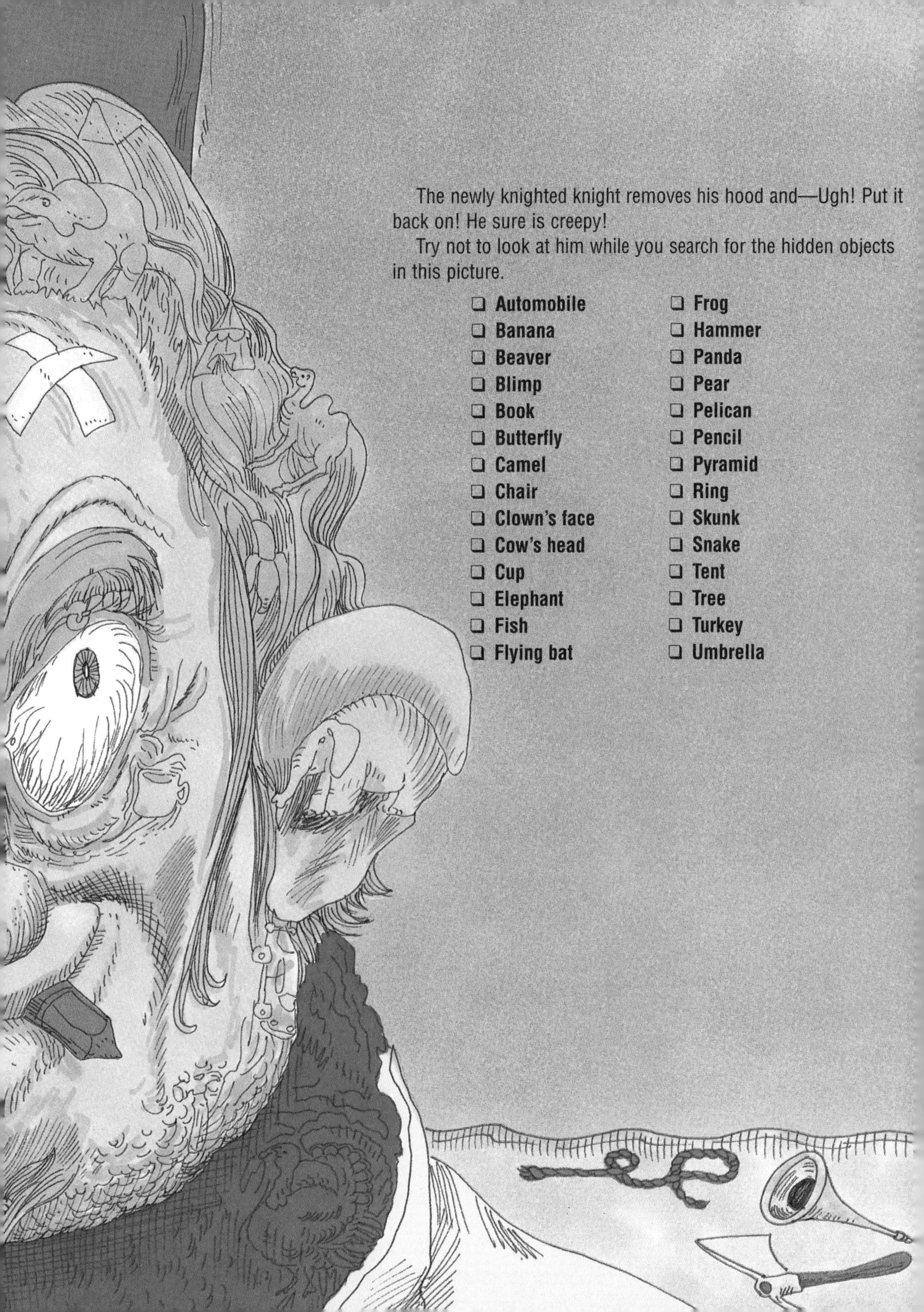

The newly knighted knight removes his hood and—Ugh! Put it back on! He sure is creepy!

Try not to look at him while you search for the hidden objects in this picture.

- ❑ **Automobile**
- ❑ **Banana**
- ❑ **Beaver**
- ❑ **Blimp**
- ❑ **Book**
- ❑ **Butterfly**
- ❑ **Camel**
- ❑ **Chair**
- ❑ **Clown's face**
- ❑ **Cow's head**
- ❑ **Cup**
- ❑ **Elephant**
- ❑ **Fish**
- ❑ **Flying bat**
- ❑ **Frog**
- ❑ **Hammer**
- ❑ **Panda**
- ❑ **Pear**
- ❑ **Pelican**
- ❑ **Pencil**
- ❑ **Pyramid**
- ❑ **Ring**
- ❑ **Skunk**
- ❑ **Snake**
- ❑ **Tent**
- ❑ **Tree**
- ❑ **Turkey**
- ❑ **Umbrella**

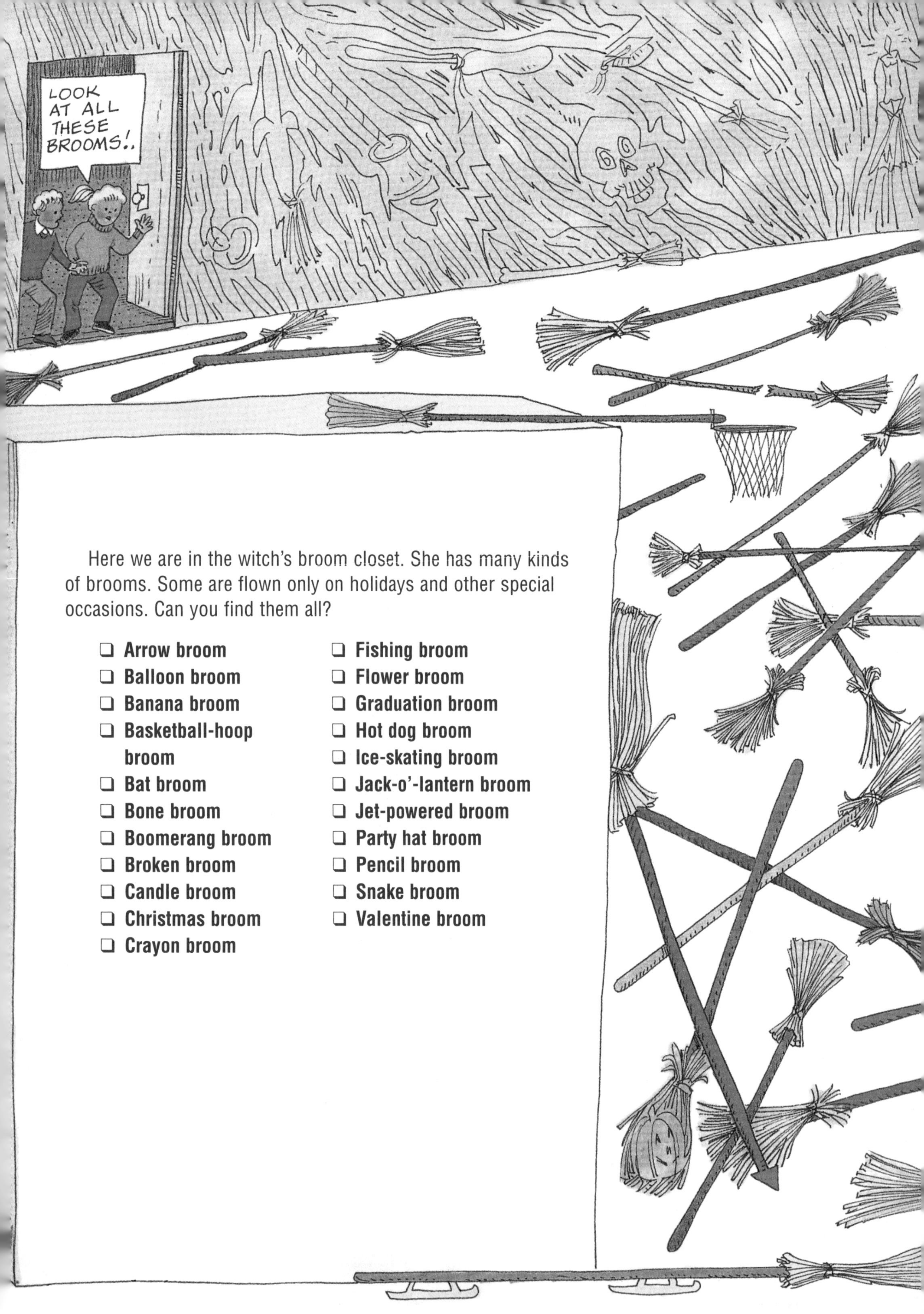

Here we are in the witch's broom closet. She has many kinds of brooms. Some are flown only on holidays and other special occasions. Can you find them all?

- ❑ **Arrow broom**
- ❑ **Balloon broom**
- ❑ **Banana broom**
- ❑ **Basketball-hoop broom**
- ❑ **Bat broom**
- ❑ **Bone broom**
- ❑ **Boomerang broom**
- ❑ **Broken broom**
- ❑ **Candle broom**
- ❑ **Christmas broom**
- ❑ **Crayon broom**
- ❑ **Fishing broom**
- ❑ **Flower broom**
- ❑ **Graduation broom**
- ❑ **Hot dog broom**
- ❑ **Ice-skating broom**
- ❑ **Jack-o'-lantern broom**
- ❑ **Jet-powered broom**
- ❑ **Party hat broom**
- ❑ **Pencil broom**
- ❑ **Snake broom**
- ❑ **Valentine broom**

WHICH OF MY WITCH BROOMS SHOULD I USE TODAY?

HE'S MAKING NIGHTMARES.

Through a hole in the wall, our friends take a peek at Wizard Merlin as he creates nasty nightmares.

Peek carefully at this picture and find the following hidden objects.

- ❑ **Airplane**
- ❑ **Apple**
- ❑ **Arrow**
- ❑ **Axe**
- ❑ **Bat**
- ❑ **Drum**
- ❑ **Elephant's head**
- ❑ **Football**
- ❑ **Ghost**
- ❑ **Gorilla**
- ❑ **Hearts (2)**
- ❑ **Helicopter**
- ❑ **Horse's head**
- ❑ **Ice-cream cone**
- ❑ **Kite**
- ❑ **Lion's face**
- ❑ **Lizard**
- ❑ **Magnet**
- ❑ **Mask**
- ❑ **Mouse**
- ❑ **Mushroom**
- ❑ **Octopus**
- ❑ **Owl**
- ❑ **Paintbrush**
- ❑ **Shark**
- ❑ **Skull**
- ❑ **Snake**
- ❑ **Top hat**
- ❑ **Toucan**
- ❑ **Windmill**

Surprise! Our fearless friends have been invited to a party in their honor. Looks like they are having a creepy, crazy good time!

You can join in the fun by finding the following hidden pictures.

- ❑ **Arrows (2)**
- ❑ **Bottle**
- ❑ **Cup**
- ❑ **Fish**
- ❑ **Flower**
- ❑ **Flying bat**
- ❑ **Fork**
- ❑ **Ghosts (2)**
- ❑ **Hot dog**
- ❑ **Ice skate**
- ❑ **Key**
- ❑ **Kite**
- ❑ **Light bulb**
- ❑ **Mitten**
- ❑ **Musical note**
- ❑ **Pencil**
- ❑ **Penguin**
- ❑ **Piggy bank**
- ❑ **Pinwheel**
- ❑ **Rocket**
- ❑ **Rocking chair**
- ❑ **Roller skate**
- ❑ **Seal**
- ❑ **Sock**
- ❑ **Spoon**
- ❑ **Toothbrush**

I WAS CROWNED PRINCESS!
13

Congratulations! You have survived Creepy Castle! But what crazy gifts have our friends brought home?
See if you can find these peculiar presents hidden in the picture below.
❑ Barbell
❑ Broken clock
❑ Cactus
❑ Dog
❑ Fire hydrant
❑ Fountain
❑ Heart
❑ Ice-cream cone
❑ Key
❑ Kite
☒ Pirate
❑ Sailboat
❑ Tennis racket
❑ Tire
☒ TV set
❑ Yo-yo
THEY'VE RETURNED FROM CREEPY CASTLE!
WHAT DO THEY HAVE?

Where's Columbus?

Christopher Columbus was born in Genoa, Italy, in 1451.

FIND BABY CHRISTOPHER BEING DELIVERED, AND THESE FUN ITEMS:

- ❑ Anchor
- ❑ Balcony
- ❑ Balloon
- ❑ Banana peel
- ❑ Broken chair
- ❑ Broom
- ❑ Candle
- ❑ Cat
- ❑ Cow
- ❑ Dog
- ❑ Flowerpot
- ❑ Green bird
- ❑ Hearts (2)
- ❑ Jester
- ❑ Kite
- ❑ Laundry
- ❑ Mouse
- ❑ Oar
- ❑ Plate
- ❑ Propeller
- ❑ Rabbits (2)
- ❑ Soccer ball
- ❑ Telescope
- ❑ Top hat
- ❑ Trunk
- ❑ TV antenna

Has the girl done her homework?
What is for sale?

HE LOOKS LIKE AN EXPLORER!
HI, LITTLE GUY!
QUIET, CHRISTOPHER, OR I'LL DROP YOU IN THAT CABBAGE PATCH!
WHERE ARE WE?
GO EAST... NO, WEST... NO, SOUTH... NO, NORTH!
WHAT'S GOING ON?
WHAT'S ALL THAT NOISE UP THERE?
IT'S A BOY!
LOOK! UP IN THE SKY!
IT'S A BIRD!
WE DON'T HAVE PLANES!
BABY, HO!
IS IT THE FAST PIZZA DELIVERY SERVICE?
Z-Z-Z-Z-!
WELCOME TO GENOA
EAT AT VITO'S
NOT FOR SALE
BABIES GIVE ME A HEAD-ACHE!
I FEEL HAPPY!
DO NOT PICK!

When Columbus was young, some people believed that ships fell off the world's edge and into the mouths of giant sea creatures.

FIND COLUMBUS AT THE STORY-TELLING SCENE, AND THESE FUN ITEMS:

- ❑ Apple
- ❑ Arrow
- ❑ Ball
- ❑ Candle
- ❑ Chef
- ❑ Crocodile
- ❑ Dogs (2)
- ❑ Earmuffs
- ❑ Feather
- ❑ Fish (3)
- ❑ Flowerpot
- ❑ Flying bat
- ❑ Goggles
- ❑ Ice-cream cone
- ❑ Musician
- ❑ Paintbrush
- ❑ Pie
- ❑ Pot
- ❑ Roller skater
- ❑ Screwdriver
- ❑ Snowman
- ❑ Spoon
- ❑ Squirrel
- ❑ Sword

Who is Uncle Zeke?
What is Alma doing?

GET ME OFF THIS!
PUFF!
I WANT TO GO HOME!
YOU MADE MY DAY!
THIS RUINED MY MEAT-LOAF!!
I SHOULD HAVE FLOWN!
I QUIT!
WE'LL BE LATE FOR DINNER!
I SHOULD HAVE STAYED IN SCHOOL!
WOW!
I'M GOING BACK TO TRANSYLVANIA!
Z
KER-PLUNK! OFF THE EDGE!
ULP!
VERY INTERESTING!
WHERE AM I?
ARF!
DID YOU SEE ELVIS?
RETREAT!!
I'M NOT GOING!
I'M NOT GOING ON ANY VACATION!
THAT'S EXCITING!
GULP!
I'M JUST VISITING!
A VIKING!
WE DON'T HAVE TV YET.
WE DON'T HAVE ELECTRICITY!
WE DON'T EVEN HAVE PIZZA!!
HOW ABOUT FAST FOOD?
SURE! EAT AT VITO'S AND THEN RUN OUT WITHOUT PAYING THE BILL!
THERE'S NO PLACE LIKE HOME!!

Christopher Columbus was the oldest of five children.

FIND COLUMBUS AS A YOUTH AT HIS FATHER'S WORKPLACE, AND THESE FUN ITEMS:

- ❑ Bottle
- ❑ Carrot
- ❑ Clothespin
- ❑ Comb
- ❑ Crayon
- ❑ Fish
- ❑ Flower
- ❑ Football
- ❑ Grapes
- ❑ Hammer
- ❑ Hearts (4)
- ❑ Horse
- ❑ Hourglass
- ❑ Ice skate
- ❑ Keys (3)
- ❑ Mice (4)
- ❑ Moth
- ❑ Necktie
- ❑ Pirate
- ❑ Ring
- ❑ Saw
- ❑ Scissors
- ❑ Sheep (2)
- ❑ Toothbrush
- ❑ Turtle
- ❑ Yo-yo

What was Christopher's father's occupation?
Who is late?

WHEN I WAS A TEENAGER...
DID THEY HAVE ROCKS THEN?
LET THE GOOD TIMES BEGIN!
WOOL WEAVER
FATHER, MAY I BORROW THE CART FOR THIS EVENING?
DO YOU WANT TO BUY A TREASURE CHEST?
SALE!
NO! YOU HAVE TO BABYSIT YOUR BROTHERS TONIGHT!
WE'RE VISITING THE RUSSOS TONIGHT!
YIPEEEEE! A LATE NIGHT!
OH, NO! CHRISTOPHER IS GOING TO PICK ON ME!
OH, NO! I DON'T WANT A SITTER!
YUMMY! WOOL!
BAAA!
THIS WILL BE A FUN NIGHT!

The explorer Columbus admired most was Marco Polo.

FIND COLUMBUS AS HE DAYDREAMS, AND THESE FUN ITEMS:

- ❑ Apple
- ❑ Arrow
- ❑ Baseball cap
- ❑ Bell
- ❑ Car
- ❑ Elephant
- ❑ Feather
- ❑ Fish
- ❑ Flower
- ❑ Ghost
- ❑ Ice-cream cone
- ❑ Jack-in-the-box
- ❑ Jack-o'-lantern
- ❑ Kite
- ❑ Lion
- ❑ Mouse
- ❑ Net
- ❑ Owl
- ❑ Paintbrush
- ❑ Pear
- ❑ Rabbit
- ❑ Ship
- ❑ Skull
- ❑ Stars (5)
- ❑ Tepee
- ❑ Umbrella

How long was Marco Polo's stay? What was the name of the emperor?

VISIT US AGAIN IN CATHAY, MARCO POLO!
IT'S ABOUT TIME THEY ARE LEAVING.
QUIET!
CHRISTOPHER ... IT'S TIME TO EAT!!
HEY, CHRIS! YOUR MOM'S CALLING YOU!
WHERE'S CATHAY?
IT'S CALLED CHINA, NOW.
THAT WAS 200 YEARS AGO!
I NEVER HEARD OF CHINANOW!
I WISH I HAD BEEN WITH MARCO POLO.
I WISH YOU HAD, TOO!
MARCO WAS HERE
HE PROBABLY DOESN'T BELIEVE THE WORLD IS FLAT!
POOR LAD!
HE HAS NO NEW THOUGHTS.
HE HAS NO OLD THOUGHTS.

Columbus arrived in Portugal after a ship that he was on sank after an attack by the French.

FIND COLUMBUS AMONG THE SHIP-WRECKED SAILORS, AND THESE FUN ITEMS:

- ❑ Accordion
- ❑ Arrow
- ❑ Bathtub
- ❑ Beach ball
- ❑ Birdbath
- ❑ Bone
- ❑ Books (4)
- ❑ Broom
- ❑ Crayon
- ❑ Cup
- ❑ Drums (2)
- ❑ Envelope
- ❑ Fire hydrants (2)
- ❑ Fishbowl
- ❑ Football
- ❑ Kite
- ❑ Octopus
- ❑ Paper airplane
- ❑ Periscope
- ❑ Pie
- ❑ Pizza
- ❑ Shark fins (3)
- ❑ Top hat
- ❑ Treasure chest

Where was the ship going? To what city will Columbus go next?

ABANDON SHIP!
GENOA TO ENGLAND
FOR SALE!
I CAN FIX THIS!
I GUESS THIS MEANS WE DIDN'T MAKE IT!!
I LOVE THE WAY THE FRENCH SERVE MY DINNER.
HELP! I CAN'T SWIM!
I CAN'T PLAY.
NEXT TIME, FLY!
THE COOK IS ALWAYS SAVED.
THIS WAY TO LISBON, PORTUGAL
I'M A 45 R.P.M.!
?
LEFT-OVERS.
I WAS A STOWAWAY!
I'M NOT COMING OUT!
?
IS THERE ROOM FOR ONE MORE?
TOO BAD I'M ON A DIET!
HOW TO SAIL
I'M GETTING OUT OF HERE!
I'LL LEND YOU AN ARM.
A TOAST TO COLUMBUS.
WHERE'S THE BIRD?
WHO IS GOING TO CLEAN UP THIS MESS ??
GET ME OUT OF HERE!
I'M THE FIRST ONE TO REACH SHORE.
IS ELVIS COMING?
DO I KNOW HIM?
I WON!
H2O

Columbus wanted to find the shortest route to the Indies by sailing west from Portugal, instead of sailing east.

FIND COLUMBUS IN THE TROLL'S TOLL LINE, AND THESE FUN ITEMS:

- ❑ Alligators (2)
- ❑ Apple
- ❑ Artist
- ❑ Banana peel
- ❑ Duck
- ❑ Elephant
- ❑ Flying bat
- ❑ Genie and his lamp
- ❑ Ice skates (5)
- ❑ Kangaroo
- ❑ Lost boot
- ❑ Rabbit
- ❑ Red wagon
- ❑ Roller skater
- ❑ Sacks (5)
- ❑ Sailboat
- ❑ Schoolbags (2)
- ❑ Ship in a bottle
- ❑ Skateboard
- ❑ Skier
- ❑ Snowman
- ❑ Telescope
- ❑ Turtles (2)
- ❑ Umbrella
- ❑ Walking stick
- ❑ Watering can

Who is collecting the tolls?
What is for sale?

WHAT'S THE ANSWER TO THE HOME-WORK?
THE WORLD IS FLAT!
WHAT'S THE RUSH?
WHEN DO THE OLYMPICS START?
COMING THROUGH!
I'M GOING TO BE LATE FOR SAILING TO THE NEW WORLD!
NOT ME!
IT'S CROWDED HERE! WE NEED A NEW WORLD!
WHAT'S HOLDING THINGS UP?
STOP PUSHING!
IT MUST HAVE BELONGED TO HANNIBAL.
IT'S NOT MINE.
I'M WARM.
I'M LATE FOR WORK!
I'M GOING HOME!
I'M IN NO RUSH!
WHERE?
I SEE THE EDGE!
NO-WAY
I QUIT!
ME, TOO!
GO WEST
THE WAY TO GO???
GO EAST
I CAN'T READ!
WHERE IS HE?
I'M STAYING RIGHT HERE!
CHRISTOPHER CHANGED ALL THE ONE-WAY SIGNS! WHAT WILL HE DO NEXT?
I'M NOT!
YOU DON'T KNOW WHERE YOU'VE BEEN!
HE DOESN'T KNOW WHERE HE'S GOING?
WHERE'S COLUMBUS?
H2O
I'M VISITING, TOO!
WHERE'S THE NEW WORLD?
I DON'T KNOW!
I KNOW HIM!
I THINK IT FELL OFF THE EDGE!
EVERY-BODY HOLD STILL!
OKAY!
THE WIZARD OF OZ?
WHERE?
DO THEY HAVE FLOWERS IN THE NEW WORLD?
DRAW ME.
WATCH YOUR STEP!

Portugal's rulers would not pay for Columbus's plan to sail to the Indies.

FIND COLUMBUS IN THE KING'S COURT, AND THESE FUN ITEMS:

- ❑ Axe
- ❑ Bears (2)
- ❑ Bowling ball
- ❑ Broom
- ❑ Cactus
- ❑ Camel
- ❑ Candles (2)
- ❑ Chef's hat
- ❑ Fish (2)
- ❑ Football
- ❑ Frog
- ❑ Hockey stick
- ❑ Hot dog
- ❑ Ice skate
- ❑ Igloo
- ❑ Lion
- ❑ Medal
- ❑ Paintbrush
- ❑ Pen
- ❑ Shopping bag
- ❑ Spoon
- ❑ Star
- ❑ Train
- ❑ Truck
- ❑ Turtle
- ❑ Yo-yo
- ❑ Zipper

How many jokes does the jester have?
Who was a prince?

JUAN TWO
I SENT MY DOUBLE TO FIND OUT THEIR REACTIONS!!
I THINK I'LL GO TO SPAIN!
FINISH YOUR HOMEWORK FIRST!
COME AGAIN!
HAVE A NICE TRIP!
DON'T FORGET TO WRITE!
THIS IS FOR YOUR OWN GOOD!
IS THAT A DEFINITE NO?
YOU COULD HAVE LOST YOUR HEAD!
I WANT TO GO, TOO!
EXIT
OFF WITH HIS HEAD!
HE'S NOT STAYING FOR LUNCH?!
THE WORLD WAS ALWAYS FLAT!!
WHAT'S GOING ON?
HE'S A WASTE OF TIME!
FRAUD!
RIDICULOUS THOUGHT!
AM I NEXT? I HAVE A WAY TO SPIN HAY INTO GOLD!!
THAT SOUNDS WORTHY OF AN AUDIENCE WITH THE KING AND QUEEN!
...OR IS IT-GOLD INTO HAY?

Columbus appealed to Spain's Queen Isabella and King Ferdinand for money to begin his journey. Eventually, the queen and royal treasurer gave him the funds.

FIND COLUMBUS IN SPAIN, AND THESE FUN ITEMS:

- ❑ Alien creature
- ❑ Anchor
- ❑ Baseball
- ❑ Candles (3)
- ❑ Count Dracula
- ❑ Crowns (4)
- ❑ Cups (2)
- ❑ Dart
- ❑ Feather
- ❑ Fish (2)
- ❑ Frogs (2)
- ❑ Ghost
- ☒ Giraffe
- ❑ Gold coin
- ❑ Heart
- ❑ Hot dog
- ❑ Mice (2)
- ❑ Paintbrush
- ❑ Pig
- ❑ Rabbit
- ❑ Seal
- ❑ Ship
- ❑ Snowman
- ❑ Telescope
- ❑ Worm

Who is Harold?
Who is going to shave?

THIS TIME COLUMBUS GOT HIS MONEY!!
HE'LL FALL OFF THE EDGE WITH OUR MONEY!
PRESS
I'M ON THE SCHOOL PAPER.
LET'S GIVE HIM THE MONEY, FERDINAND!!
WE CAN DO IT!
IF I'M GOING, I'LL HAVE TO SHAVE!
WELL... I DON'T KNOW.
THE WORLD WILL NEVER BE THE SAME!
WHO ORDERED PIZZA?
A WASTE OF MONEY!!
WE'LL JUST RAISE TAXES.
WE'D DO THAT ANYWAY!
GO FOR IT!!
HE'LL FALL OFF THE EDGE!
THIS WILL BE FUN!
WILL IT BE TELEVISED?

Christopher Columbus set sail on August 3, 1492, with three ships—the *Niña*, the *Pinta*, and the *Santa María*.

FIND COLUMBUS WITH HIS SHIPS, AND THESE FUN ITEMS:

- ❑ Anchor
- ❑ Barrel of monkeys
- ❑ Basket
- ❑ Black bird
- ❑ Bottles (2)
- ❑ Cactus
- ❑ Candle
- ❑ Coffeepot
- ❑ Football
- ❑ Hamburgers (2)
- ❑ Hammer
- ❑ Helmet
- ❑ Lost boot
- ❑ Lunchbox
- ❑ Mermaid
- ❑ Pig
- ❑ Pink fish (3)
- ❑ Pumpkin
- ❑ Rabbit
- ❑ Rat
- ❑ Shipwrecked sailor
- ❑ Tires (2)
- ❑ TV set
- ❑ Unicorn
- ❑ Worm
- ❑ Would-be surfer

On which ship is Columbus sailing? Which is the smallest?

?
I SEE A CROW.
YOU'RE GOING TO FALL OFF THE EDGE OF THE WORLD!
THE NIÑA IS 66 FEET LONG!
WE'RE TIED TO THE SANTA MARIA.
I WANT TO GO HOME!
THIS IS THE BEST SEAT ON THIS BOAT.
FARE-WELL.
THE SANTA MARIA IS 85 FEET LONG.
SEE YOU SOON... I HOPE!
I HOPE I'M RIGHT!
ME TOO!
I'M SEASICK ALREADY.
TO THE EDGE
DON'T GIVE UP THE SHIP!
WHAT DO YOU GET WHEN YOU CROSS A FISH WITH A RUSSIAN RULER?
A CZARDINE!
I'LL SEE YOU SOON!
QUIET! YOU'RE FRIGHTENING THE FISH AWAY!
BANDON SHIP!
I'M A ROBBER DUCKY.
HAVE FUN!
I'M DOING THE WAVE.
POOOOF!
IT'S EASY TO WEIGH FISH!
SURE! THEY HAVE THEIR OWN SCALES.

In October 1492, Columbus reached San Salvador, an island in the Bahamas.

FIND COLUMBUS ON THIS TROPICAL ISLAND IN THE NEW WORLD, AND THESE FUN ITEMS:

- ❑ Banana peel
- ❑ Book
- ❑ Clothespin
- ❑ Clown
- ❑ Dog
- ❑ Duck
- ❑ Feather
- ❑ Football
- ❑ Ghost
- ❑ Ice skates
- ❑ Kite
- ❑ Lizard
- ❑ Lost mitten
- ❑ Mice (2)
- ❑ Oars (6)
- ❑ Painted egg
- ❑ Pencil
- ❑ Pig
- ❑ Rabbit
- ❑ Scarecrow
- ❑ Seesaw
- ❑ Snail
- ❑ Snake
- ❑ Stars (3)
- ❑ Train engine
- ❑ Turtle
- ❑ Wooden leg

Who wants a cracker?
Who is all wet?

DID WE FALL OFF THE EDGE YET?
WHY DO I ALWAYS HAVE TO ROW?
CLEAN WATER ZONE
I THINK THIS IS THE WRONG SPOT!
THIS MUST BE ASIA!
NO. I DON'T THINK SO.
CAN WE HAVE THIS DAY OFF?
YES!
THIS IS A GREAT PLACE FOR A WINTER VACATION!
IT'S TOO FAR!
I CLAIM THIS PLACE FOR THE KING AND QUEEN OF SPAIN!
ARE THEY STAYING FOR LUNCH?
I'M NEVER GOING ON ANOTHER SEA VOYAGE AGAIN!!
YOU'RE NOT COMING BACK WITH US?
IT'S ONLY BEEN 70 DAYS!
WE'VE SAILED MORE THAN 4,000 MILES OF OCEAN!
I THINK IT'S TIME YOU TOOK A BATH!
LET'S START BACK!
IS HE SHORE-SICK?
DID ANYONE BRING ME A CRACKER?
BRING THE SOAP!

Upon Columbus's return, he was named Admiral of the Ocean Sea and Viceroy of the Indies. On September 25, 1493, he set sail on his second journey to the New World, with 17 ships and about 1,000 men.

FIND COLUMBUS AS THE SHIPS SET SAIL, AND THESE FUN ITEMS:

- ❑ Arrow
- ❑ Baseball bat
- ❑ Birds (2)
- ❑ Broom
- ❑ Camel
- ❑ Candle
- ❑ Cooking pot
- ❑ Fish (3)
- ❑ Flying bat
- ❑ Fork
- ❑ Ghost
- ❑ Heart
- ❑ Mouse
- ❑ Pen
- ❑ Quarter moon
- ❑ Seal
- ❑ Snowman
- ❑ Star
- ❑ Tent
- ❑ Toothbrush
- ❑ TV antenna
- ❑ Upside-down tree

How many ships sailed this time?
Who did not escape from the zoo?

LET'S EAT!
ARE WE GOING AGAIN?
SURE! WE DIDN'T FALL OFF THE EDGE OF THE WORLD LAST TIME, WE MUST TRY AGAIN!
I'M ON MY BREAK!
THIS VESSEL IS CROWDED!
I HAVE TO SLEEP STANDING UP!
I'M GOING.
I'M GOING ACROSS ON A BARREL!
THIS TIME YOU'RE GOING TO FALL OFF THE WORLD!
ARE THEY LEAVING AGAIN?
I CHANGED MY MIND!
I WANT TO GO, TOO!
I'M FEELING A BIT WOBBLY!!

WHAT'S WRONG AT SCHOOL?

Monday morning. A new week of school begins with an enjoyable bus ride through town. Before the students arrive at school, can you find at least 13 things that are wrong with this picture?

IS IT MONDAY ALREADY?
WE HAVE A NEW STUDENT BUS DRIVER!
OOPS! I JUST LOST MY HOME-WORK PAPERS!
I FORGOT MY LUNCH!
I'M HUNGRY!
WAIT FOR ME!
THIS IS BETTER THAN A ROLLER COASTER!
I THINK I'M LOST!
I'M TAKING A SHORTCUT!
STUFF-IS-US!
STOP
HONK!
HONK!
KEEP YOUR EYE ON THE BALL!
OOOPS!
IT'S MOBY DICK!
I DON'T REMEMBER PASSING THIS WAY BEFORE!
NO FISHING

Classes are about to start. Right before the bell rings, "It" sees 15 wrong things in the school yard. Do you?
"IT" LOOKS FAMILIAR!
I FORGOT MY BOOKS!
I SAW ELVIS IN THE SCHOOLYARD LAST WEEK!
I'M A GRADUATE!
I'M GOING HOME!
ARE YOU SURE THIS IS A SCHOOL DAY?
HI, JOE!
I DON'T WANT ANYONE TO KNOW THAT I GO TO SCHOOL HERE!
I DON'T WANT ANYONE TO KNOW THAT EITHER!
I'M THIRSTY!

I'M SHOW!
I'M TELL!
LAST STOP!
I BROUGHT "IT" LAST YEAR!
DOES HE WANT MY COOKIE?
I BROUGHT "IT" FOR SHOW AND TELL!
YIPES! I FORGOT TO BRING MINE!
UGH! I'M SUPPOSED TO PLAY THIS TUBA WHILE MARCHING !?!
CAN "IT" PLAY BASKETBALL?
?
COACH
I'M GOING OUT FOR THE BASKETBALL TEAM AS SOON AS I'M 4 FEET TALL!
DOES "IT" HAVE A HALL PASS?
I'M TRYING OUT FOR THE TRACK TEAM!

The first lesson of the day is arithmetic. But what's wrong here? Search for and find at least 12 things that are wrong in this classroom.

A
B
C
D
E
F
G
H
7
+8
16
7
+8
15
7
+8
17
ONE OF YOU IS CORRECT!

Special school programs are always interesting and a lot of fun. But there are at least 20 things wrong with this assembly. Can you find them?

HURRY UP WITH THE INTRODUCTIONS, I'M GOING ON A SAFARI!
I'M DUE ON MARS IN 2 MINUTES!
HOW'S THE WEATHER DOWN THERE?
I HAVE A TICKET FOR YOU FOR DOUBLE PARKING!
IS THERE A PATIENT IN THE HOUSE?
MY SHIP CAME IN!!
SPECIAL POGRAM TODAY
I WANT TO BE AN ASTRONAUT!
I WANT TO BE A SINGER.
WAIT FOR ME!
I'M HUNGRY!
WHAT DID YOU BRING FOR LUNCH?
PEANUT BUTTER AND JELLY!
NO! I DON'T HAVE A CARROT!
OINK!
AHOY!
I'M A LATE KNIGHT!
I'M COMING!

The annual school play is scheduled to begin in a few days. However, there are a few things wrong with this full-dress rehearsal. Look for exactly 10 of them.

"ALAS, POOR YORICK! I KNEW HIM"... BUT I DON'T KNOW MY LINES!
I LIKE THIS PROP!
I LIKE HAMLET!
I LIKE HAM AND EGGS!
I DON'T LIKE THE COLORS!
IT'S NOT REALISTIC.
I'M IN THE WRONG SHOW!
TO YELLOW BRICK ROAD
THE PLAY NEEDS MORE REHEARSAL!

The Arts and Crafts Club is meeting in room 221. Everything is under control—or is it? Find at least 12 things that are out of control and wrong with this picture.

YOU MADE MY NOSE TOO BIG!
I THINK ONE SLEEVE IS TOO LONG!
MY ROBOT WORKS!
ROOM 222
WILL IT FLY?
THIS IS THE WAY TO DO IT!
I AM HUNGRY!
I-I'M-D-DIZZ--D-DIZZY!
SMILE.
IT'S FOR THE BIRDS!
PINE CONES

Lunchtime! The students can't wait to dig into all that great food! Seek and find at least <u>13</u> things that are wrong in this lunchroom.

EXIT ONLY
SCHOOL LUNCH MENUE
FRESH FISH
TRY ME!
HOT DOG
MYSTERY PIZZA
by DUMBINO
BEANS
I'LL HAVE ONE OF THESE!
HOLD MY PLACE IN LINE. I'LL BE RIGHT BACK!
FILL IT UP!
NEXT!
WHAT'S FOR DESSERT?
SNACK!
MAKE MY DAY!
COME ON JOEY! I'LL SAVE YOU A SEAT!
I HAD A PERFECT SCORE ON THE EXAM!
WHAT? A ZERO?
RESERVED
DID I TAKE ENOUGH?
YUM... GOOD!
?
YOU ACTUALLY SPOKE TO FRANKIE?
YES, I DID!
HE'S SO CUTE!
CAN I SIT HERE?
YOU SURE CAN!

Today is the day of the big test. Exams aren't really that difficult if you've studied for them. If you haven't, you'll have many wrong answers. Can you find 12 things that are wrong here?

I WANT TO GO HOME!
THIS IS NOT TOO BAD!
BRAINS, DO YOUR THING!
I COMPLETED THE EXAM!
FASTER-FASTER!
THIS IS NOT THAT HARD.
I CAN DO IT... I CAN DO IT... I *DID* IT!
ALL DONE!
I SHOULD HAVE STUDIED!
I SHOULD HAVE STAYED IN KINDERGARTEN!
WE SHOULD NOT HAVE EXAMS!
THIS IS A SNAP!
?
I LOST MY APPETITE!
HMMM.. 77 PLUS 10 EQUALS 90?
BRING ON MORE EXAMS!
I WISH IT WAS TOMORROW!
BLANK!

Gym is most students' favorite class. Mixed in with all the exercise, sports, and games are at least 18 wrong things for you to find. Go to it!
WHERE DID HE GO?
?
WHERE DO YOU WANT THIS?
IT'S A GOOD VIEW FROM UP HERE!
AM I RUNNING IN THE RIGHT DIRECTION?
VERY GOOD, CLASS!
HERE I COME, READY OR NOT!
FEET DO YOUR THING
MY FEET ARE TOO FAR AWAY!
HERE'S MY FIRST PITCH!
PLAY BALL!
UMPIRE

RUN!
RUN!
PUFF!
THIS IS SIMPLE!
GRUNT!
MOVE IT!
I'M NEXT!
HURRY UP AND SHOOT!
WE ARE IN THIS ISSUE!
SPORTS ILL-STATED
I CAN'T DO THAT!
OK! EVERYONE JOG!
15-16-17-18-21-22-24-25-27-
THINGS LOOK DIFFERENT!
THIS COULD BE THE START OF MY CAREER!
FIRE AWAY!

This year, the class trip is to Prehistoric Times Amusement Park. The dinosaur slide looks like fun! Find at least 15 things wrong with this picture.

STEP RIGHT UP, KIDS. NO PUSHING!
I'M NEXT!
IT'S NIGHT-TIME!
THIS IS WILD!
THIS WAY ONYL
ONE WAY
SPACE FOUR RENT!
STEP RIGHT UP, KIDS. NO PUSHING!
CAN I HAVE YOUR AUTOGRAPH ?
TICKKETS
THAT WAS FUN!
LET'S DO IT AGAIN!
PARK OPENS 9 AM
DUNNOSAUR SLIDE
?
DO YOU LIKE THIS, FRED?
I SURE DO, BARNEY!

Another week of school has ended. Some students are staying for after-school activities. Before the rest leave for home, there are at least 18 wrong things here for you to find.

WHICH WAY DO I GO?
I CAN WALK HOME!
UNGH! PUFF!!
I HOPE THE BUS DRIVER KNOWS THE WAY HOME TODAY!
THIS IS NOT GOING TO WORK!
YOU'RE DOING A GOOD JOB, JOHNNY!
STOP
I BEARLY PASSED THE EXAM!
YOU LOOK CUTE IN YOUR UNIFORM.
I GOT 100 IN MATH!
THAT'S GREAT!
WE'LL SEE YOU AGAIN!
BYE!

ANSWERS

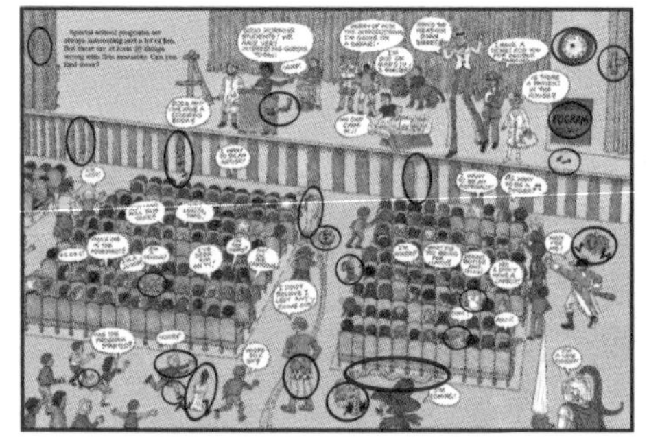

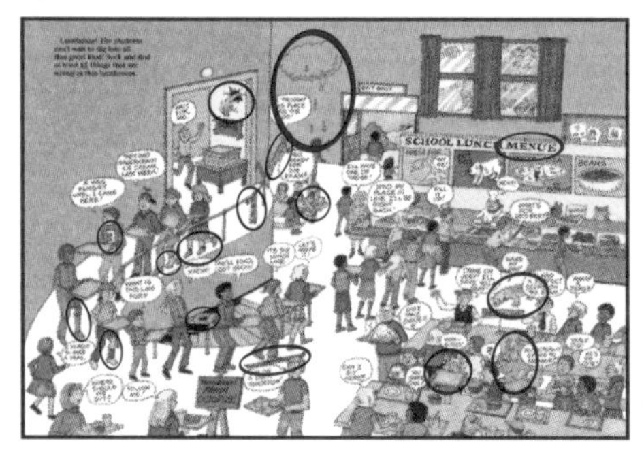

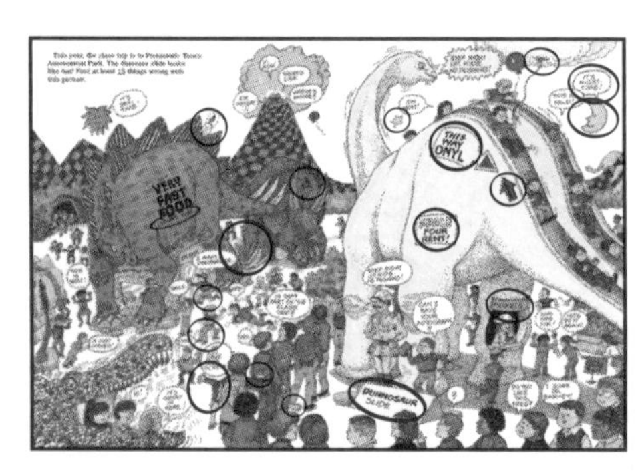

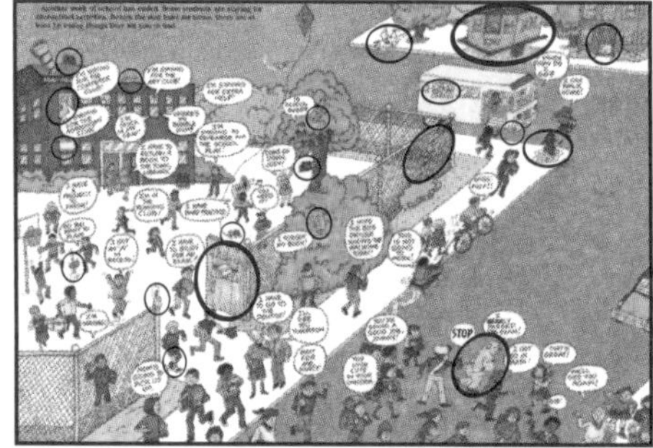

WHAT'S WRONG IN THE HAUNTED HOUSE?

The children have discovered a real haunted house! Who's going to be brave enough to enter? You'll find out on the next page. But first, what's wrong here? At least 15 things. Can you find them?

EXIT
13
DO DROP IN... IF YOU DARE!
FOR RENT
DO NOT DISTURB

Everyone is afraid to enter the house except Bob and Bobbie. Before they open the front door, find at least 15 things that are wrong with this picture.
I WOULDN'T GO INSIDE!
I'M AFRAID!
THIN ICE
I FELL!
ME TOO!
TOMORROW WE'LL TELL THE TEACHER WHY THEY ARE ABSENT!
GOOD IDEA!
GOOD LUCK!
SO LONG!

FOR RENT IF YOU DARE
LET'S GO IN FIRST!
WE'RE NOT AFRAID!
WRING BELL
CLOSE DOOR BEFORE ENTERING!
THIS END UP

As the old, squeaking door slowly swings open, the boys hear lots of strange sounds and see at least 13 wrong things in the room. Do you?
BOO!
GET ME OUT OF HERE!
DRIP! DRIP!
CREAK!

CLOSE THE DOOR!
I FEEL A DRAFT!
G-G-GO ON IN.....!!
E-E-EVERYTHING IS F-F-FINE!
DO COME IN
POP!

All the children follow Bob and Bobbie into the house. In the living room they see 13 ghosts! First find them. Then try to find at least 6 things that are wrong with this picture.
TICK-TOCK-TICK-TOCK!
CAP
A
B

BOO!
WOW! LOOK AT THIS!
WOW!
WATCH YOUR STEP
GHOST CROSSING ZONE!

The children peek into the kitchen, where a witch is stirring up a foul-smelling brew. But what's wrong here? Look for at least 13 things that are wrong in the witch's kitchen.
DRIP!!
THIS IS MY FAVORITE RECIPE!
IT'S JUST LIKE MY MOTHER'S COOKING...600 YEARS AGO!
BLUB-BLUB-BLUB!
R-R-R-R-R
WITCHES FAST-FOOD
BONE SOUP!
BAT WING BROTH
IS IT SOUP YET?

I LOVE THE COOK
CALENDAR
1605
OCTOBER
EXIT ONLY
HERE IS THE MEASURING CUP YOU ASKED FOR!
GULP!
UGH!
IT SMELLS ICKY!
IT SMELLS LIKE YOUR SOCKS!
HOLD YOUR BREATH!!
YUM!
DUMB!
CRUMB!
GUM!
DRUM!
STRUM!

A giant skeleton drops in on the kids! Every scared one of them scrambles to get out. Before they do, search for and find at least 10 things that are wrong with this picture.

WHICH WAY IS THE EXIT?
COME IN HERE!!
IT'S A SECRET PASSAGE!
SQUEAK!
DONG! DONG! DONG! DONG!
GO!! GO!!! GO!!!
GET ME OUT OF HERE!

The children escape through a secret passage that leads to a dingy dungeon. It is home to a hard-to-forget dragon. There are lots of things wrong in the dungeon—exactly 15. Can you find them?
I HAVE STOMACH BURN!
IT MUST HAVE BEEN THAT FOREST FIRE I ATE!
I MIGHT BE HUNGRY!
DRAGON
POP!

HOME SWEET HOME
LET'S GET AWAY FROM HERE!
HE LOOKS BIG!
HE LOOKS HUNGRY!
WHAT AM I DOING HERE?
DON'T SIT ON ME!
WE HAVE VISITORS!
YUM!

Bob and Bobbie gather their friends together for a meeting. The creatures in the house all seem to be hungry. Before the children share their milk and cookies, find at least 12 things that are wrong in this picture.

I FEEL MUCH BETTER!
YUMMY!
OOOOOH! CAN I HAVE YOUR RECIPE?
I'M A SCHOOL SPIRIT AND I LOVE COOKIES AND MILK!
SIA
I WANT SOME TOO!
MAY I PLEASE HAVE SOME?

After snack time, the creatures and the children decide to play some games. Seek and find at least 10 wrong things here before they play Hide and Seek.
BOO!
BOO!
BOO!
BOO!
BOO!
BOO!
I FORGOT HOW TO BECOME A BAT!!
HELP!
HE WON'T SEE ME NOW!
RUN-RUN! HIDE-HIDE!
I'M NOT READY!
YUM!! THIS TASTES GOOD!
WHERE SHOULD I HIDE?
THIS IS A GOOD HIDING PLACE!!
THIS IS FUN!

I'M READY! HE WON'T FIND ME!!
I DON'T WANT TO PLAY!
HOLD THAT DOOR!
DID SOMEONE KNOCK?
WAIT! I'M NOT READY!
HE'LL NEVER FIND ME HERE!
HE WON'T FIND ME!
HERE I COME, READY OR NOT!!
I'M A GHOST-IN-THE-BOX!
VACANCY

The friendly fiends ask the children to help them fix and clean the haunted house. Look at the mess in this room and find at least 10 things that are wrong.

I'LL CHANGE THE LIGHT BULB!
DOWN WITH COB WEBS!
I'LL TAKE THE OLD PAINT OFF THE WALL!
CAN I GIVE YOU A HAND?
I'LL CLEAN OUT THE CRYPT!
I NEVER THOUGHT OF USING MY BROOM THIS WAY!
WHAT DO I DO WITH ALL THIS DUST?
I CAN FIX THIS!
BB
I'D RATHER FLY!
I'LL CLEAN THE DUNGEON.
I'M GETTING OUT OF THIS CLEAN HOUSE!

The house is soon fixed, cleaned, and painted, both inside and out. It looks so good that no one will ever believe it was a genuine haunted house. We know better! But there are still at least 10 wrong things here for you to find.

COME UP AND SEE ME SOME-TIME!
COME ON IN!
BOO!

ANSWERS

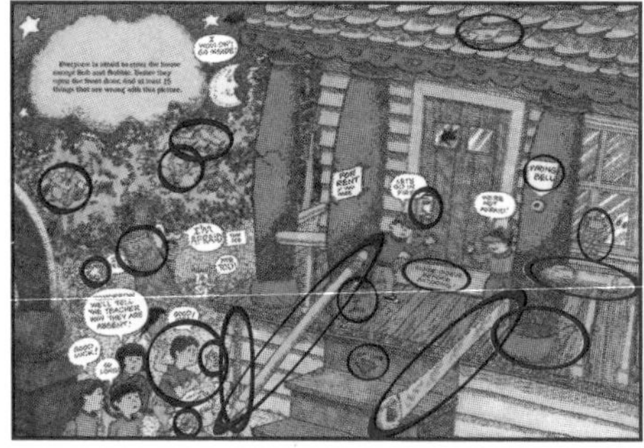

WHAT'S WRONG AT THE AMUSEMENT PARK?

The Fun Park Amusement Center is officially open for wrongdoing. You are invited to find 10 things that have gone wrong on opening day.

UGLY MOUNTAIN RIDE
FUN FOOD
FUN HOUSE HIGH SCHOOL
I ALREADY ATE!
THAT'S MY KIND OF HIGH SCHOOL!
WELCOME TO FUN PARK
HA-HA-HA! THIS IS SILLY!

The first stop is the Wacky Little Schoolhouse. Come inside and help find at least 10 things that are wrong here.
THIS IS A WACKY SCHOOL!
HONOR GRADUATE
THIS IS GREAT!
I'M NEXT!
TEACHER
THIS IS MY KIND OF SCHOOL!

NO HOMEWORK TODAY... OR EVER!
TODAYS MATH EXAM ANSWERS
1-307
2-1486
3-X=7
PLAY TIME SCHEDULE
ALL DAY!
PIZZA FOR LUNCH!!
OH! I ONLY RECEIVED AN "A+++++++!"
GEE! I GOT AN "EXCELLENT!"
WOW! I'M AN "A" STUDENT!
PICK-A-GRADƎ
APPLES FOR THE STUDENTS
CAPTAIN COOL?
THIS IS COOL!
COMIC BOOK
SUPER DUPER

The flume ride is almost ready to go—
except for a few things that are wrong.
Can you find exactly 12 things that are
wrong with this picture?
SPLASH!
SPLASH!
THE END IS NEAR.
I THOUGHT IT WAS ALMOST OVER.
YOU'RE NEXT! DO YOU HAVE ANY FINAL WORDS?
G-G-GOOD B-BYE!
GOING UP!
WHICH WAY IS UP?
ONE WAY
FLUMES -R- US

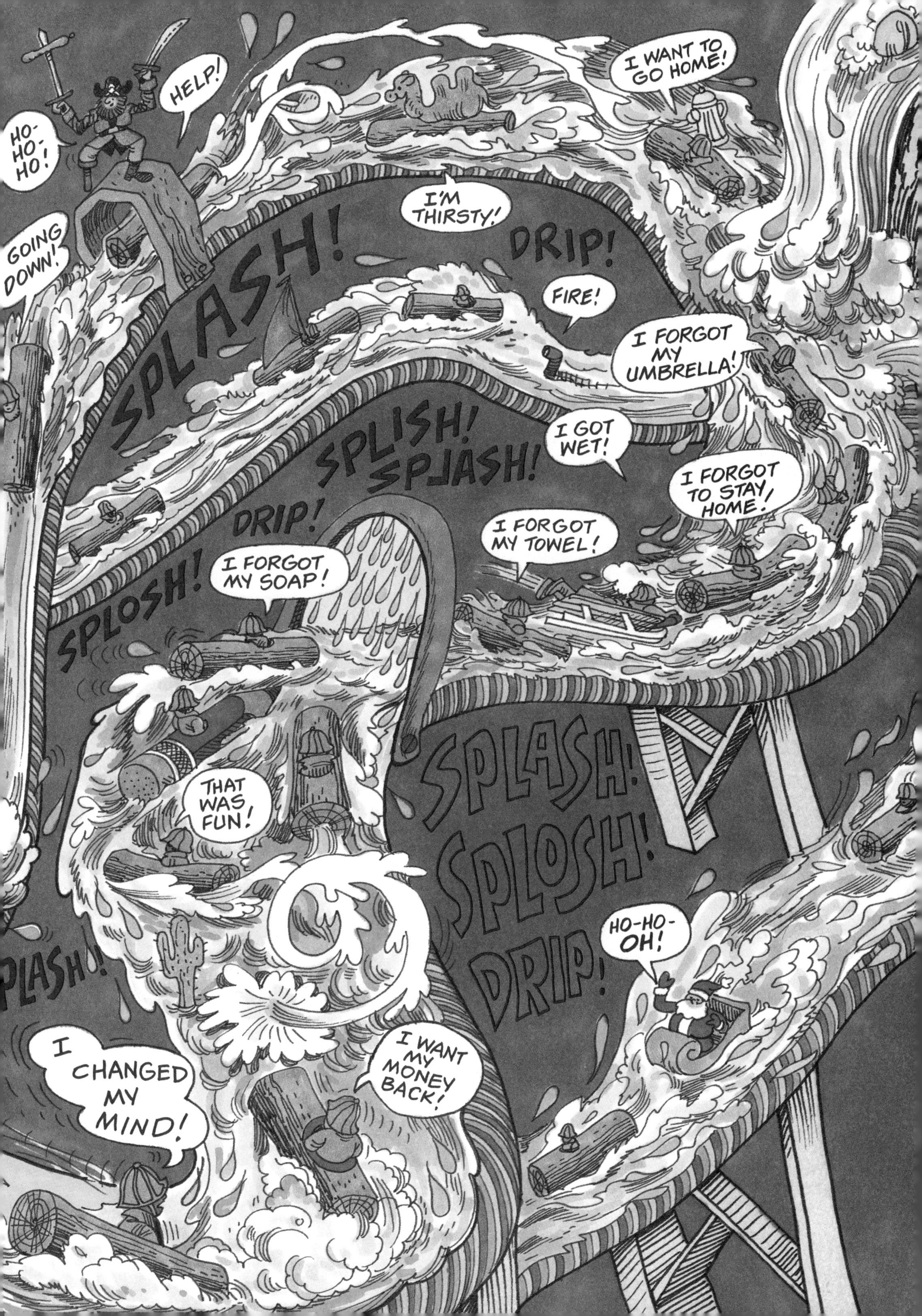

HO-HO-HO!
HELP!
I WANT TO GO HOME!
I'M THIRSTY!
GOING DOWN!
SPLASH!
DRIP!
FIRE!
I FORGOT MY UMBRELLA!
SPLISH! SPLASH!
I GOT WET!
DRIP!
I FORGOT TO STAY HOME!
I FORGOT MY TOWEL!
SPLOSH!
I FORGOT MY SOAP!
SPLASH!
SPLOSH!
DRIP!
THAT WAS FUN!
HO-HO-OH!
PLASH!
I CHANGED MY MIND!
I WANT MY MONEY BACK!

No amusement park is complete without its very own wacky circus. How many wrong things can you find here?
THIS IS THE GREAT WACKY CIRCUS!

THIS IS NOT MY DAY!
HARRY! YOU FORGOT TO PUT OUT THE GARBAGE!
THE SHOW IS ON!
I'M LOST!
HAVE FUN!
I'M LOOKING FOR MY ARROW!
IT'S HARD TO HAVE THIS SUIT PRESSED!!
I'M HUNGRY.

You have just stepped into the Fun House. Along with the laughs, there are 10 things here that are wrong. Find them.
HA-HA!
HEE-HEE!
HO!
HO-HO-HO
HA-HA!
I WANT TO GO DOWN THERE!
THE SIGN WAS RIGHT!
I THINK SOMEONE IS WATCHING ME!!
I'M GOING UP!
STAIRS TO NO PLACE
HOW DO YOU LIKE MY FLOWER?
IT'S ALL WET!
YOU LOOK GREAT!

HERE WE GO!
HA-HA!
EE-HEE!
THE LIGHTS WENT OUT!
IT'S DARK IN HERE!
HA-HA-HA!!
HA-HA-HA-HA-HA-HA-HA-HA-HA-HA-HA-HA-HA-HA!!
HO-HA-HEE-HO!
HA!
HA-HA-HA!
VERY FUNNY!
HEE-HEE!
HA-HA-HO!
HO-HO-HO!
TICKLE ZONE
HA!
SMILE
THIS IS FUN!
FLYING PIE ZONE
MY FAVORITE FLAVOR!
BULLS EYE!
THAT'S GREAT!
JACK
WE LANDED IN BUBBLES!
HEE-HAW!

Welcome to the wildest roller coaster ever! Besides the thrills and chills, there are 10 things wrong with this ride for you to find.

BUMPY ROAD AHEAD
OH!
LET ME OFF! I HAVE TO GET MY HAT!
WHOOOOSH H!!!
CLICKITY-CLICKITY-CLICKITY-CLICKITY!
I'M GLAD I DIDN'T GO ON **THAT!**
OH!
OH!
OH!
OH!
OH!
NO!

The Tunnel of Terror—where you can find ghosts, monsters, and at least 18 things that are wrong.

NO EXIT
EVER!
I'M HUNGRY! DOES ANYONE HAVE A DONUT?
IT MUST BE SOMETHING I ATE!
I'M COLD IN HERE!
YOU WON'T BE FOR MUCH LONGER!
WHEW! IT HAS BAD BREATH!
WHERE IS THE YELLOW BRICK ROAD?
HSSSS!

The amusement park is filled with fun things to do. But before you can enjoy yourself, search for and find at least 18 things that are wrong with this picture.
FUN
ARCADE
LOOK AT THE BIRDIE!
SMILE!
YOU LOOK SILLY!
YOU LOOK SILLY!
I LIKE TUNA FISH!
I LIKE GOLDFISH!

THIS MAKES ME HUNGRY!
IT MUST BE FOR A FLEA CIRCUS!
RED IS MY COLOR!
WHICH WAY IS UP?
I'M NEXT!
OH!
OH! OH!!
THERE'S NINA AND ROBERTA!
I WANT TO GO ON THE MERRY-GO-ROUND!
I'M NOT GOING IN THAT!

Today, the children's zoo is open. Everyone enjoys petting and playing with the animals, and finding at least 15 wrong things.
I SURE WILL.
WAIT FOR ME!!
GIVE MY BEST TO MR. ED!
I'M GOING TO FEED THE BUNNY!
IT'S CHOW TIME AGAIN!
IS IT MORNING YET?
HOW CUTE!
OINK!
I'M EXPECTING DONALD, TODAY.
Z
Z

I FEEL FUNNY TODAY!
YOU LOOK FUNNY!
CLUCK, CLUCK!
DID ANYONE BRING ME A FRESH SOCK?
WHEN WILL THIS HATCH?
I'M WAITING FOR SANTA!
?
2
DON'T BE SO NEAT, JUNIOR!

Have your tickets ready, please! The Toot-Toot train ride has begun. Along the way, look for and find at least 18 things that are wrong with this picture.
TOOK-TOOT!
LIVE VOLCANO NO SMOKING ALLOWED!
I'M JOE OF THE JUNGLE!
MAKE MY DAY!
WHERE'S THE ICE?
DO YOU HAVE A RESERVATION
JUNGLEVILLE
CAVEMAN CAVE INN
THAT'S ME!
BIG FOOT TERRITORY
TOOT-TOOT!
DIP

AVALANCHE AHEAD
FALLING ZONE ROCK
LANDING ROCK ZONE
GHOSTVILLE POPULATION
PEOPLE — 0
GHOSTS — 5
WELCOME TO DERAILEDVILLE
ARE YOU ON SCHEDULE?
ZIG ZAG ZONE
BUMPS AHEAD!

The last event of the day is a ride on the Ferris wheel. Unfortunately, there are a number of things wrong here. How many can you find?

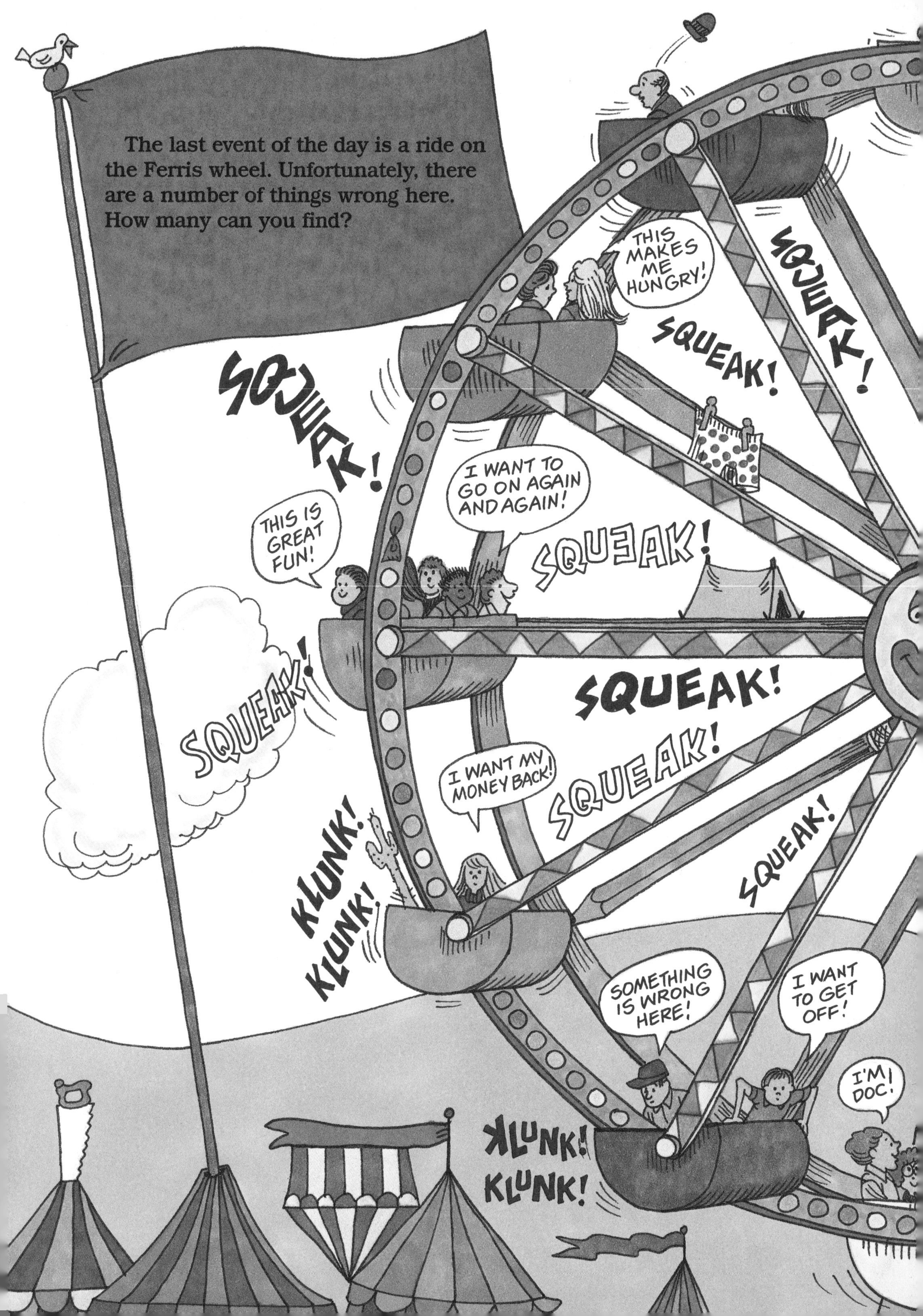

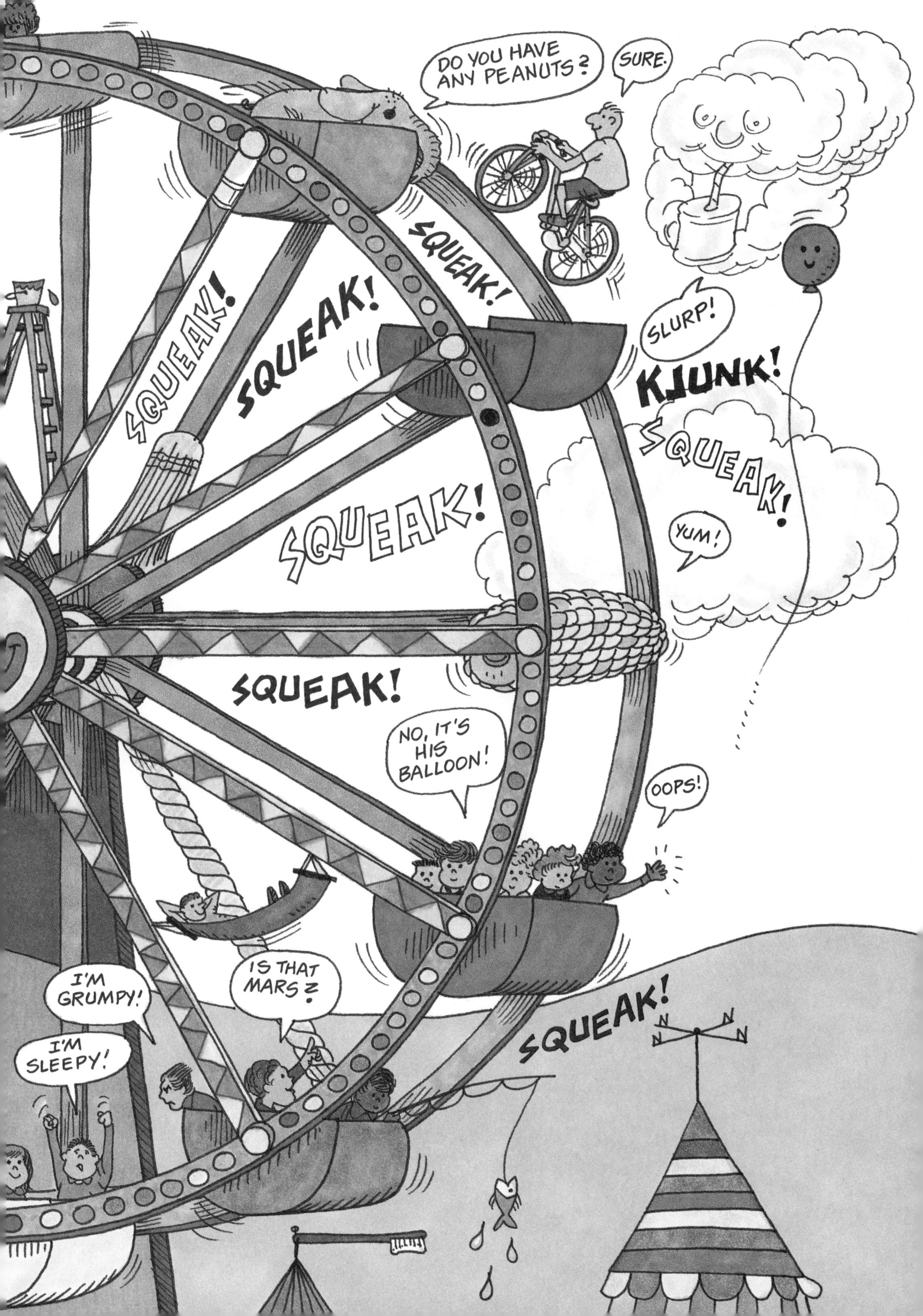
DO YOU HAVE ANY PEANUTS?
SURE.
SQUEAK!
SQUEAK!
SQUEAK!
SLURP!
KLUNK!
SQUEAK!
SQUEAK!
YUM!
SQUEAK!
NO, IT'S HIS BALLOON!
OOPS!
I'M GRUMPY!
IS THAT MARS?
I'M SLEEPY!
SQUEAK!
N N N N

ANSWERS

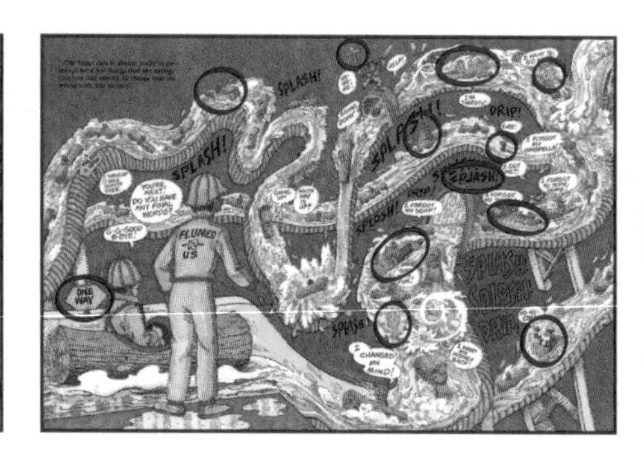

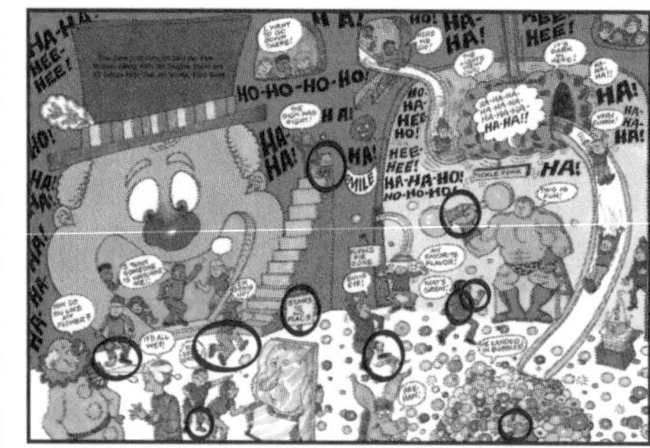

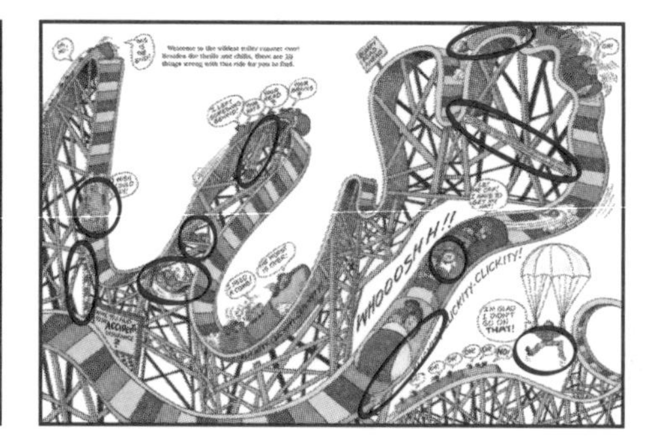

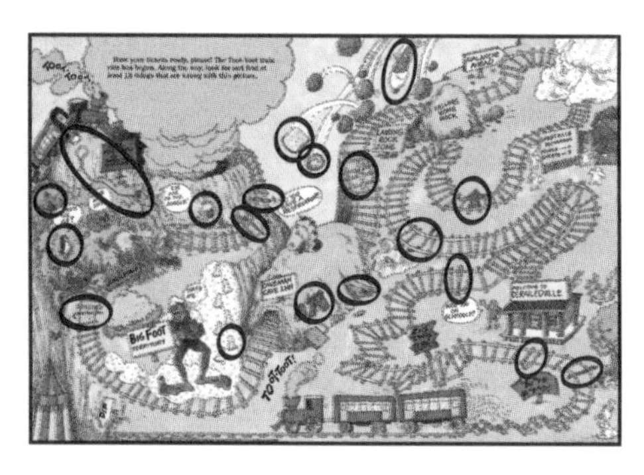

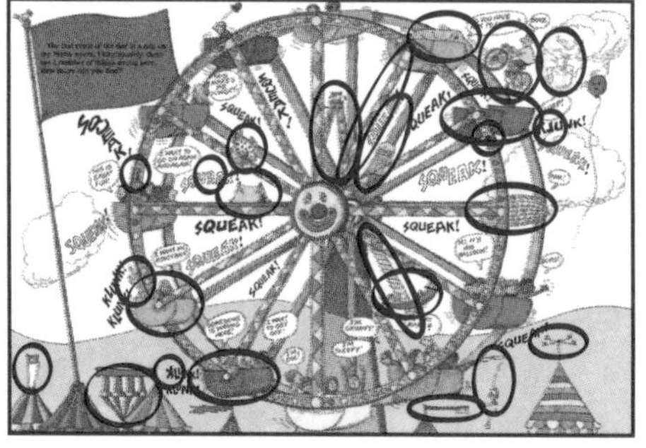

WHAT'S WRONG AT THE MOVIES?

It's movie time! Let's all go see our favorite flick! But first, find at least 12 things that are wrong with this picture.

CINEMA
6 UGH!...RUN!!
7 BUNNY HONEY
8 GRUNT
9 ROBIN HOOD
10 SLAP STICK
NOW PLAYING

OH, NO! IT'S THE KIDS' MATINEE!
TICKUTS
Z.
NO PUSHING!
ONE ADULT TICKET!
I'LL PICK YOU UP AFTER THE MOVIE IS OVER!
LET'S MOVE IT!
HI, RUSTY!

The time is 1849. The place is the American West. The movie studio has spent $100,000,000 to make this film as accurate as possible. However, 11 wrong things have slipped past the director. Can you find them?
HOWDY!
I LIKE THE COWBOY!
I LIKE THE INDIAN!
I LIKE THE POPCORN!

HI!
I'D LIKE TO TAKE A NAP!
I LIKE THE SCENERY!
I LIKE THE HORSE!

Captain Zipp matches his super powers with the Gang That Couldn't Do Right. What's wrong here? Can you find at least 12 things?
ZOUNDS!! I'VE GOT YOU!
YOU CAN SEE THE WIRES THAT MAKE HIM FLY!
HE'S STILL MY FAVORITE!
BUT HE REALLY CAN'T FLY!
NEITHER CAN YOU!

WHO IS THAT?
OH, NO! IT'S CAPTAIN ZIPP!!
RUN, DON'T WALK!
I DIDN'T DO IT!!
WAKE ME WHEN IT'S OVER!
WHAT TIME IS IT?
TIME TO LEAVE!
THIS MOVIE IS A DUD!

The Ninjas are getting ready to do battle on the big screen—and you are seeing it! Can you also see 10 things that are wrong with this picture?

NINJA CITY WATƎR TOWER
ARF!
LET ME LOOK AT MY SCRIPT!
I QUIT!
HELP! HELP! HELP!
QUIET!
GO-RATSO!
I WANT TO SIT CLOSER TO THE SCREEN!
SAVE THE GIRL!!
SAVE THE FILM!

The great detective Sheerluck Homes is featured in his 249th movie. The old boy is searching for that famous criminal, Professor Moranutty. What he *should* be searching for is all the things that are wrong in this picture. How many can you find?

PROFESSOR MORANUTTY IS NOT HERE!
I WOULDN'T BRAG ABOUT THAT!
HEY, SHEERLUCK! LOOK IN THE TRUNK!!

A typical day in space. As the spacecraft approaches the planet Sha-Quab, an astronaut drops in for a visit. But suddenly, 10 wrong things appear in this picture. Your mission is to find them!
THAT PLANET IS A GIANT BALLOON!
I'M GLAD I'M NOT IN THIS FILM!
ME TOO!
THIS IS AWFUL!
THIS MAKES ME SEE SICK!
I LIKE IT!
PLEASE KEEP YOUR HAT ON!
WHO WROTE THIS STORY?
NO ONE!
I ALREADY SAW THIS ON TV!
I DON'T WANT TO SEE THIS!
I'M GOING HOME!

SPACE TOUR
HI, JOE!
WHO'S YOUR FRIEND?
HI, XYRZ!
HAVEN'T I SEEN YOU SOMEWHERE ELSE?
I'M HUNGRY!
Z-Z-Z-Z!!
IS SHE PART OF THE MOVIE?
IT'S NOT GETTING MY CONE!
YOU CAN'T HAVE MY POP CORN!
IT'S ONLY A MOVIE!
WAKE ME UP WHEN IT'S OVER!
I SAW THIS BEFORE...IN A *BAD DREAM*!
I'M GOING HOME TO DO MY HOMEWORK!
I WANT MY MONEY BACK!
I'M GOING HOME TO DO THE DISHES!
I SHOULD HAVE STAYED HOME!
I GIVE UP!

I'M LOST! WHICH WAY IS TOKYO?
I'M HUNGRY!
I'M GOING FISHING!
I HAVE A TOOTH-ACHE!
I NEED A SHAVE!
I CAN'T SEE!
THIS MUST BE THE MONSTER MOVIE!
IT'S ALREADY STARTED!
SIT DOWN!
DOWN IN FRONT!

DOES ANYONE IN THE AUDIENCE HAVE SOME PEANUTS?
HOW ABOUT POPCORN?
QUIET! YOU WOKE ME UP!
I'M IN THE WRONG MOVIE!
Hurry up and sit down! The monster movie has begun. But before you are too comfortably settled in your seat, take a good look and find what's wrong here: exactly 13 things.

Today's cartoon feature is *Honey Bunny Goes Planting.* A few things have gone wrong here. Can you find at least 10 of them?
I'M GERRY, THE FLYING GIRAFFE!
WAIT FOR ME!
WAIT FOR ME... I'LL WATCH!
ME TOO!
GO AND PLANT CARROTS, HONEY BUNNY!
WE'LL DIG THEM UP AND EAT THEM!
THEY MUST BE THE BAD GUYS!

WHERE ARE WE GOING?
TO HONEY BUNNY'S HOUSE!
HI-HO... HI-HO, IT'S OFF TO PLANTING I GO!
OINK!
I'M CUTE TOO!
THANK YOU, MY DEAR!
I LOVE THE WACKY PENGUIN!

Grunt—the movie everyone has been waiting for—is now playing at your favorite theater. It's about the world's longest marathon. There are at least 13 things wrong with this race for you to find.
I QUIT!
THIS IS ABOUT US.
I WANTED TO BE IN A WESTERN!
ME TOO!
I THINK I'M BEING FOLLOWED
I WANT TO WIN!
I WON! I WON!
START
10 MILES TO GO!

WAIT FOR ME!
I FINALLY BROKE INTO SHOW BUSINESS!
FIFTY MILES TO GO!
OUCH!
QUIET.
TOOT-TOOT!
HELP!
I'M THE STAR OF THIS FILM... I WIN!!
HI, MOM!
HI, DAD!
THIS MOVIE SHOULD HAVE BEEN NAMED "PUFF-PUFF!"
THAT WASN'T IN THE SCRIPT!
Z-Z-Z-Z!
I'M TIRED JUST FROM WATCHING!
IT'S A REALLY BIG CAST OF ACTORS!

In this movie, Robin Hood and Little John are fighting over the right to cross the log bridge first. Look for and find at least 15 things wrong with this picture.

YE CASTLE
OOPS!
NOTTINGHAM TOWN
I HOPE HE BROUGHT HIS TOWEL!
I HOPE HE BROUGHT DRY CLOTHES!
I HOPE IT GETS BETTER!

This old-time silent movie has many things wrong with it. Can you find at least 18?
WHAT HAPPENED TO THE COLOR?
I HAVEN'T GOT IT!
I DIDN'T DO IT!

CATSUP
I CAN'T HEAR WHAT THEY'RE SAYING!
NEITHER CAN I!!
THIS IS AN OLD BLACK AND WHITE MOVIE MADE BEFORE THEY KNEW HOW TO PUT SOUND INTO FILMS!

ANSWERS

CINEMA
1 HI-HO TEXAS
2 CAPTAIN ZIPP
3 NINJA MICE
4 SHERBLUCK HOMES
5 SPACE LEMON
NOW PLAYING
CINEMA
6 UGH!...RUN!!
7 BUNNY HONEY
8 GRUNT
9 ROBIN HOOD
10 SLAP STICK
NOW PLAYING

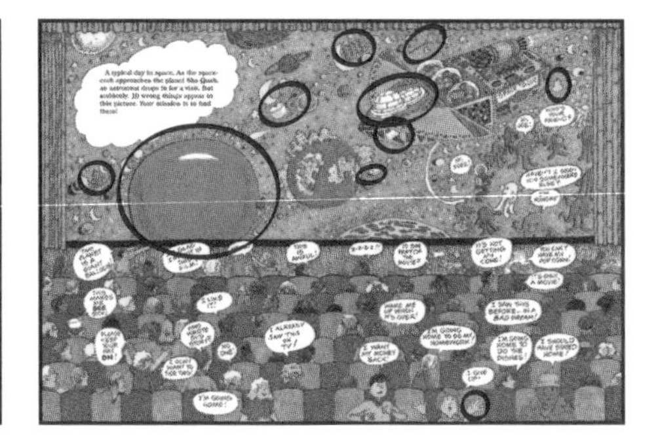

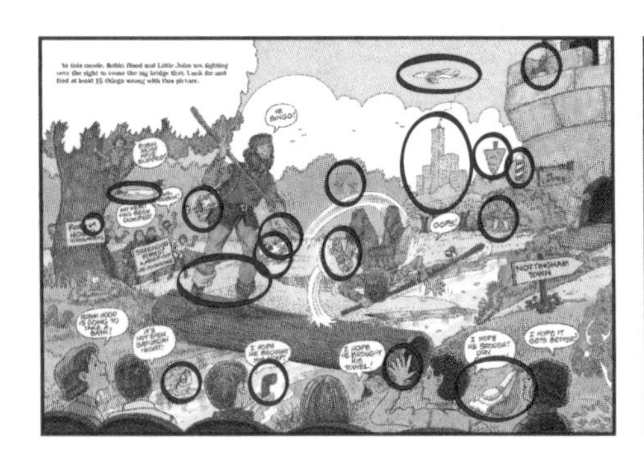

LOOK & LOOK AGAIN DINOSAURS

FAST-FOODASAURUS

FIND THESE ITEMS:

- ☐ Banana peel
- ☑ Bell
- ☐ Beret
- ☐ Bones (2)
- ☐ Book
- ☐ Bow tie
- ☐ Broken balloon
- ☑ Cactus
- ☐ Candle
- ☐ Chef
- ☐ Crayon
- ☐ Envelope
- ☐ Eyeglasses
- ☐ Fish (2)
- ☐ Flower
- ☐ Flying bat
- ☑ Football
- ☑ Heart
- ☐ Key
- ☐ Lost sock
- ☐ Mouse hole
- ☐ Mushroom
- ☐ Music note
- ☐ Net
- ☐ Rabbit
- ☐ Saw
- ☐ Scarf
- ☐ Star
- ☐ Sunglasses
- ☐ Tattoo
- ☐ Toothbrush
- ☐ Umbrella
- ☐ Whistle

DOES THEIR DRIVE-THROUGH WINDOW STAY OPEN LATE AT NIGHT?
WHY, DOES YOUR CAR GET HUNGRY AROUND MIDNIGHT?
LOOK, THEY'RE HAVING A SPECIAL ON BRONTO BURGERS!
YUM!
FREE INDIGESTION
THERE'S A FLY IN MY SODA!
DON'T WORRY! THE SPIDER ON YOUR STRAW WILL GET IT!
HAVE THEY STOPPED SERVING BREAKFAST?
NO, BUT WE BEGGED THEM TO!
WITH OR WITHOUT CHEESE.
I'M REALLY HUNGRY!
MOM
WHAT'S THE DIFFERENCE BETWEEN THE REGULAR BURGER AND THE DELUXE BURGER?
ABOUT A CUP OF GREASE!
MAYBE WE SHOULD HAVE USED THE DRIVE-THROUGH!
NO! I HATE TALKING INTO THE SAUROPOD'S MOUTH!
NO, I LOVE THE ATMOSPHERE!
WHAT DO YOU EXPECT WITH A ONE-YEAR-OLD BURGER?
WISH IT A HAPPY BIRTHDAY!
I FOUND A RUBBER BAND IN MY BURGER! WHAT DOES IT MEAN?
I DON'T KNOW, I'M NOT A FORTUNE TELLER!

FAMILY REUNION PORTRAITASAURUS

FIND THESE ITEMS:

- ☐ Baseball
- ☐ Baseball bat
- ☐ Baseball caps (2)
- ☐ Cactus
- ☐ Candle
- ☐ Coffee cup
- ☐ Coffeepot
- ☐ Cookie
- ☐ Dino ordering pizza
- ☐ Egg
- ☐ Eyeglasses
- ☐ Football
- ☐ Fish
- ☐ Flower
- ☐ Heart
- ☐ Horseshoe
- ☐ Mouse
- ☐ Moustache
- ☐ Paintbrush
- ☐ Pear
- ☐ Ring
- ☐ Rollerskate
- ☐ Sleeping dino
- ☐ Stars (2)
- ☐ Straw
- ☐ Yo-yo

ARE WE GOING TO POSE FOR THE PHOTOGRAPHER?
NO, WE'RE GOING TO RUN AROUND THE STUDIO AS FAST AS WE CAN!
YOU KNOW WHAT WOULD MAKE A GREAT PORTRAIT?
A SHOT WITHOUT YOU IN IT?
I DON'T LIKE WHAT I'M WEARING. I'LL BE RIGHT BACK!
MAYBE WE SHOULD TAKE THIS PHOTO OUTSIDE.
I'D LIKE TO ORDER 25 PIZZAS TO GO!
IMAGINE IF WE TRIED TO HAVE OUR PORTRAIT PAINTED!
LET'S GO TO DINOLAND AND HAVE OUR PHOTO TAKEN ON THE ROLLER COASTER!
THAT'S BECAUSE YOUR EYES ARE RED!
THIS IS TAKING TOO LONG. I'M LEAVING!
MY EYES ALWAYS COME OUT RED IN PHOTOS!
I WANT THREE 8 X 10'S AND SEVEN WALLET-SIZED!
YOU DON'T EVEN OWN A WALLET.
I HAVE A TENDENCY TO BLINK WHEN I HAVE MY PHOTO TAKEN!
WHAT'S OUR MOTIVATION FOR THIS SHOT?
I HOPE HE HAS A SUPER-WIDE-ANGLE LENS ON THAT CAMERA!
Z-Z-Z!
WEAR SUNGLASSES!
THAT YOU WANT TO GO HOME AND GET THIS OVER WITH!
I SHOULD HAVE BROUGHT MY CAMERA!
I HOPE THE PHOTOGRAPHER ISN'T GETTING PAID BY THE HOUR.
WE SHOULD FORM A DINOSAUR PYRAMID!
LET'S TAKE THE PHOTOGRAPHER'S PICTURE.

SKI-A-SAURUS MOUNTAIN

FIND ALL THE LETTERS OF THE ALPHABET:

- ☐ A
- ☐ B
- ☐ C
- ☐ D
- ☐ E
- ☐ F
- ☐ G
- ☐ H
- ☐ I
- ☐ J
- ☐ K
- ☐ L
- ☐ M
- ☐ N
- ☐ O
- ☐ P
- ☐ Q
- ☐ R
- ☐ S
- ☐ T
- ☐ U
- ☐ V
- ☐ W
- ☐ X
- ☐ Y
- ☐ Z
- ☐ Baseball hat
- ☐ Flower
- ☐ Heart
- ☐ Pizza delivery dino
- ☐ Star

I HEARD THAT THE LAST TIME YOU WERE HERE YOU STARTED AN AVALANCHE!
YES, I MADE THE MISTAKE OF SNEEZING WHILE ATOP THE MOUNTAIN!
ARE YOU GOING TO STAND THERE AND POSE... OR SKI?
POSE!
DO YOU WANT TO GO SKIING TONIGHT?
NO, THANKS. I HAVE A HARD ENOUGH TIME DURING THE DAY!
I NEED TO GO INSIDE AND THAW OUT!
HAVE YOU TAKEN MY PICTURE?
WHY, IS IT MISSING?
HOW DO I STOP?
DO YOU KNOW HOW TO KEEP THE THERMOMETER FROM DROPPING?
USE A GOOD NAIL?
WHERE'S MY ORDER?
I DON'T SKI A LOT. I HAVE A PROBLEM WITH FALLING AND TUMBLING!
WHERE IS THE WIND WHEN IT DOESN'T BLOW?
?
AREN'T YOU GLAD YOU CAME SKIING WITH ME TODAY?!
OH, YES, THIS IS SO MUCH BETTER THAN BEING INSIDE IN FRONT OF A WARM FIRE!

THE DUNCE-A-SAURUS CLUB

FIND THESE ITEMS:

- ☐ Apple
- ☐ Banana peel
- ☐ Barber pole
- ☐ Baseball bat
- ☐ Birdcage
- ☐ Cactus
- ☐ Capless dino
- ☐ Cupcake
- ☐ Fire hydrant
- ☐ Fish
- ☐ Flower
- ☐ Ghost
- ☐ Golf club
- ☐ Ice-cream cone
- ☐ Kite
- ☐ Mailbox
- ☐ Mouse hole
- ☐ Mustaches (2)
- ☐ Paintbrush
- ☐ Pencil
- ☐ Quarter moon
- ☐ Rabbit
- ☐ Ring
- ☐ Scarf
- ☐ Seal
- ☐ Star
- ☐ Tepee
- ☐ Thermometer
- ☐ Watermelon slice
- ☐ Whale

WHEN DOES THIS CLUB MEET?
EVERY SEVENTH TUESDAY OF THE MONTH!
WHY ARE YOU WEARING BINOCULARS?
I LOST MY EYEGLASSES!
?
WHY DOES THIS CLUB MEET HERE?
HOW MANY GUESSES DO I GET?
IS THAT YOUR OFFICIAL DUNCE CAP?
I'M NOT WEARING A CAP!
WHO ARE YOU CALLING?
YOU...BUT YOU'RE NOT HOME!
WOULD YOU LIKE ME TO TELL YOU ABOUT THIS CLUB?
SURE...I COULD USE A GOOD LAUGH!
YES, BUT NOW I CAN'T TURN IT OFF!
I'M PROUD OF BEING A DUNCE!
ARE YOU A MEMBER OF THIS CLUB?
NO, I JUST LOVE WEARING THIS CAP!

SHOP-A-HOLIC SAURUS

FIND THESE ITEMS:

- ☐ Arrows (5)
- ☐ Books (2)
- ☐ Bird
- ☐ Broken bulb
- ☐ Bubble gum bubble
- ☐ Cane
- ☐ Cap
- ☐ Coffee cup
- ☐ Earmuffs
- ☐ Fish
- ☐ Football
- ☐ Lost balloon
- ☐ Lost sock
- ☐ Mailbox
- ☐ Music note
- ☐ Newspaper reader
- ☐ Pencil
- ☐ Phonograph
- ☐ Rocking chair
- ☐ Scarves (2)
- ☐ Shoulder bag
- ☐ Star
- ☐ Tires (4)
- ☐ Trash cans (2)
- ☐ Umbrella
- ☐ Vacant store
- ☐ Volcano
- ☐ Water fountain

NO, I'M HAVING EVERYTHING SHIPPED.
WHEN I GET HOME, I THINK I'LL SHOP ONLINE.
HOW MANY SHOPPERS DOES IT TAKE TO CLEAN OUT A STORE?
ONE, IF IT'S MY WIFE!
CRETACEOUS SHOES
KENTOSAURUS MART
NOASAURUS
WHERE'S THE SKI SHOP?
HOT LAVA SALE
?
SINCE I SPEND SO MUCH TIME IN THIS MALL... I WAS THINKING ABOUT GETTING A JOB HERE.
JUST ONE MORE STORE!
YOU SAID THAT TEN STORES AGO!
I THINK I'LL GO BACK AND LOOK AT THAT DRESS I SAW THREE HOURS AGO.
HOW DO YOU REMEMBER WHAT IT LOOKED LIKE?
WHY SHOULD THEY NAME THIS MALL AFTER YOU?
BECAUSE I SPENT MOST OF MY MONEY HERE... I PRACTICALLY OWN IT!
BUT THEY WERE SUCH A BARGAIN!
WHY DID YOU BUY TIRES? WE DON'T HAVE A CAR!
NOW COMES THE FUN PART... TRYING TO REMEMBER WHERE I PARKED THE CAR.
WALKING AROUND THE MALL IS THE ONLY EXERCISE I GET!
REACHING INTO MY WALLET IS THE ONLY EXERCISE I GET!
IS YOUR GIRLFRIEND A MAGICIAN?
YES, SHE CAN MAKE MERCHANDISE DISAPPEAR

MT. VOLCANOSAURUS

FIND THESE ITEMS:

- ☐ Automobile
- ☐ Banana
- ☐ Bath brush
- ☐ Beachball
- ☐ Boot
- ☐ Carrot
- ☐ Clothespin
- ☐ Cow
- ☐ Cowboy hat
- ☐ Crayon
- ☐ Daisy
- ☐ Dart
- ☐ Fish
- ☐ Flying bat
- ☐ Football
- ☐ Ghost
- ☐ Hockey stick
- ☐ Humpty Dumpty
- ☐ Keys (2)
- ☐ Kite
- ☐ Lightbulb
- ☐ Mitten
- ☐ Octopus
- ☐ Pumpkins (2)
- ☐ Rabbit
- ☐ Rooster
- ☐ Sand pail
- ☐ Sock
- ☐ Telescope
- ☐ Television
- ☐ Umbrella

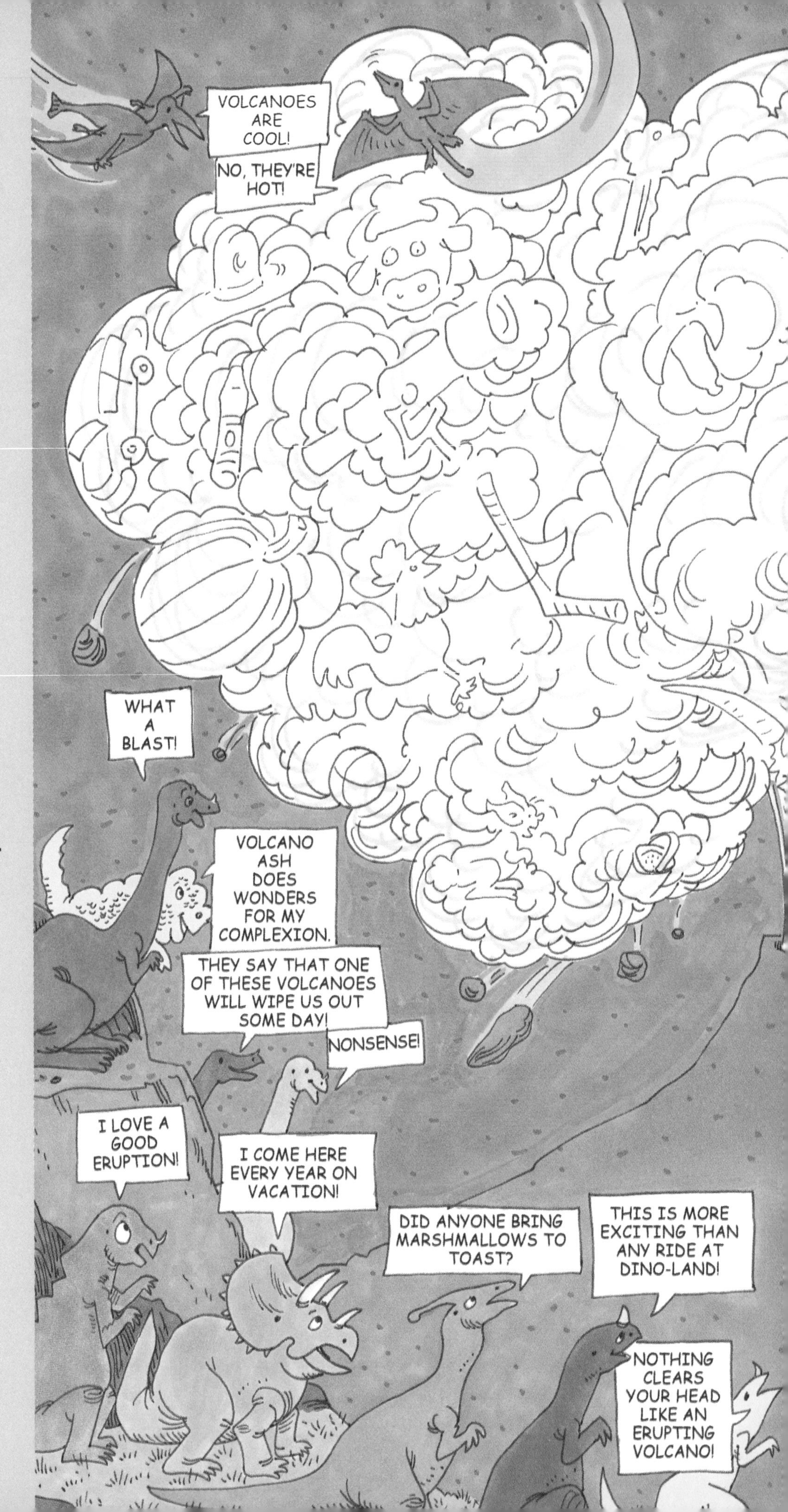

WHEN'S THE SECOND SHOW GOING TO START?
WHO ORDERED PIZZA WITH EXTRA LAVA?
I SHOULD HAVE BROUGHT MY VIDEO CAMERA!
WHAT A THRILL!
WE SHOULD DO THIS MORE OFTEN!
UP, UP, AND AWAY!
IT'S MOTHER NATURE AT HER BEST!

HOLLYWOOD-A-SAURUS

FIND THESE ITEMS:

- ☐ Arrows (2)
- ☐ Baseball cap
- ☐ Beret
- ☐ Bones (2)
- ☐ Bouquet of flowers
- ☐ Burned-out bulb
- ☐ Dino ordering pizza
- ☐ Escaped balloon
- ☐ Feather
- ☐ Football
- ☐ Ice-cream cone
- ☐ Hammer
- ☐ Heart
- ☐ Hot dog
- ☐ Lost shoe
- ☐ Microphone
- ☐ Moustache
- ☐ Pearl necklace
- ☐ Pencil
- ☐ Pizza
- ☐ Scissors
- ☐ Screwdriver
- ☐ Stars (2)
- ☐ Sunglasses (2)
- ☐ Telescope
- ☐ Yo-yo

WHEN DO TICKETS GO ON SALE FOR THE 73RD AWARDS?
THEY ALREADY DID... AN HOUR AGO.
I WONDER IF MOVIE STARS GET FREE POPCORN WHEN THEY GO TO THE MOVIES?
HOLLYWOOD LOVES FELIX!!
HI!
HOW DO I GET INTO A MOTION PICTURE?
JUST BUY A TICKET LIKE EVERYBODY ELSE.
I READ THAT SHE HAS MORE FELIX AWARDS THAN FANS.
I READ THAT SHE KEEPS ALL OF HER AWARDS IN A SPECIAL CLIMATE-CONTROLLED ROOM.
IS THE AWARD NAMED AFTER A CAT?
YOU DO REALIZE THAT FELIX IS AN AWARD... NOT A LIVING CREATURE!
I'M LOOKING FOR THE REAL STARS.
I JUST FLEW IN FROM CHICAGO TO ATTEND THIS AWARD SHOW.
YOUR ARMS MUST BE VERY TIRED!
THESE STARS DON'T LOOK AS BIG AS THEY DO ON THE SCREEN.
TRICK PHOTOGRAPHY.
I GOT HIS AUTOGRAPH LAST YEAR.
I DIDN'T KNOW HE COULD WRITE!
I'D LOVE TO BE IN THE MOVIE BUSINESS!
I HEAR THIS THEATER IS HIRING USHERS.
ANYBODY WANT MY AUTOGRAPH?
IT'S JUST AN HONOR TO BE NOMINATED!
WHEN ARE THEY GOING TO LET US IN THE THEATER?
OUR TICKETS ARE FOR OUTSIDE VIEWING ONLY.
HERE'S DINO!
ANYONE WANT MY AUTOGRAPH?
THAT MOVIE STAR JUST WAVED AT ME!
I THINK HE WAS SWATTING A FLY.

AIRPORT-A-SAURUS

FIND THESE ITEMS:

- ☐ Accordion
- ☐ Arrow
- ☐ Book
- ☐ Bow tie
- ☐ Candy cane
- ☐ Crown
- ☐ Eyeglasses
- ☐ Flying carpet
- ☐ Flying elephant
- ☐ Flying fish
- ☐ Flying saucer
- ☐ Football
- ☐ Hat box
- ☐ Heart
- ☐ Hot-air balloon
- ☐ Hot dog
- ☐ Ice-cream pop
- ☐ Kite
- ☐ Paper airplane
- ☐ Periscope
- ☐ Pizza box
- ☐ Propellers (2)
- ☐ Roller skates
- ☐ Sailor cap
- ☐ Star
- ☐ Straw
- ☐ Top hat
- ☐ Umbrella
- ☐ Watering can
- ☐ Yo-yo's (2)

WHAT HAPPENED WHEN YOU WENT TO COMPLAIN ABOUT YOUR LOST LUGGAGE?
I FOUND A PILOT WEARING MY CLOTHES!
I ALWAYS GET ILL THE NIGHT BEFORE A TRIP!
MAYBE YOU SHOULD TRY LEAVING A DAY EARLIER!
WHERE ARE YOU HEADED TODAY?
NOWHERE, IF THIS LINE DOESN'T MOVE!
CHECK IN
DO YOU WANT THE AISLE OR WINDOW SEAT?
BOTH!
WHY AREN'T THERE CEILING FANS IN PLANES?
THIS MUST BE THE PLACE!
CAN YOU TELEPHONE FROM A PLANE?
OF COURSE I CAN TELL A PHONE FROM A PLANE!
IT'S A GREAT DAY FOR FLYING!
I WOULDN'T KNOW... I'VE BEEN WAITING HERE FOR THE LAST HOUR!
WHY DIDN'T YOU BRING ANY LUGGAGE?
I'M STILL WAITING FOR THE AIRLINE TO RETURN MY BAGS FROM MY LAST TRIP!
I LOVE TO TRAVEL!
ME TOO... IT'S THE WAITING AROUND I DISLIKE!
YOU CHECKED IN 12 PIECES OF LUGGAGE FOR A THREE DAY TRIP?
ONE IS MINE... THE REST BELONG TO MY WIFE!
ARE YOU FLYING FOR BUSINESS OR PLEASURE?
NEITHER!

SENIOR-CITIZENSAURUS

FIND THESE ITEMS:

- ☐ Anchor
- ☐ Apple
- ☐ Balloon
- ☐ Balls (2)
- ☐ Banana
- ☐ Bow tie
- ☐ Canes (2)
- ☐ Coffeepot
- ☐ Coonskin cap
- ☐ Crown
- ☐ Cup
- ☐ Drum
- ☐ Eyeglasses (4)
- ☐ Feather
- ☐ High-heeled shoes
- ☐ Kite
- ☐ Moustache
- ☐ Neckties (3)
- ☐ Paddle
- ☐ Paintbrush
- ☐ Pencil
- ☐ Pocketbook
- ☐ Propeller
- ☐ Ring
- ☐ Sailboat
- ☐ Sailor cap
- ☐ Skateboard
- ☐ Sunglasses
- ☐ Top hat
- ☐ Turtle
- ☐ Yo-yo

REMEMBER WHEN WE WERE KIDS?
OH... I'LL HAVE TO GET BACK TO YOU ON THAT ONE.
READING THE NEWSPAPER?
NO, THERE'S A LITTLE ANT ON THE GROUND STARING AT ME AND I'M TRYING TO BLOCK HIS VIEW.
B.C. TIMES
ROCKS INVENTED
HOW WAS YOUR TRIP TO THE MUSEUM YESTERDAY?
NO, THANKS, I'M NOT THIRSTY!
THEY ALMOST WOULDN'T LET ME GO HOME! THEY THOUGHT I WAS AN EXHIBIT!
GAME ROOM
WHAT WERE YOU LIKE AS A CHILD?
SHORT AND YOUNG!
I DON'T WANT TO WALK IN MY SLEEP.
THE DOCTOR SAID YOU NEED A NEW PAIR OF EYE-GLASSES!
I WANT A SECOND OPINION.
OKAY, YOU NEED A NEW HAT, TOO!
HOW CAN I KEEP THIS NEIGHBORHOOD BEAUTIFUL?
MOVE!
SHARE YOUR WISDOM WITH ME, GRANDPA.

CYBER-SAURUS

FIND THESE ITEMS:

- ☐ Apple core
- ☐ Baseball
- ☐ Baseball bat
- ☐ Cactus
- ☐ Drum
- ☐ Elephant
- ☐ Eyeglasses
- ☐ Fish
- ☐ Flower
- ☐ Ghost
- ☐ Hamburger
- ☐ Hearts (3)
- ☐ Horse
- ☐ Igloo
- ☐ Jester
- ☐ Knitting needle
- ☐ Laundry
- ☐ Lion
- ☐ Mouse
- ☐ Moustache
- ☐ Net
- ☐ Oil can
- ☐ Pencil
- ☐ Penguin
- ☐ Plunger
- ☐ Rabbit

IT WOULD HELP IF YOU HAD AN EMAIL ADDRESS!
CRASH!
MY COMPUTER KEEPS CRASHING!
SEND IT TO DRIVING SCHOOL!
WHIRRRRRRRRRRR!
OUR JOBS ARE VERY REPETITIOUS!
YOU CAN SAY THAT AGAIN!
PING!
YOU RAN A LOT OF OTHER COMPUTER BUSINESSES?
YES! RIGHT INTO THE GROUND!
WHIRRRRRR!
IT WHISTLES A TUNE EVERY NOW AND THEN!
WHAT DID WE DO BEFORE COMPUTERS?
WALKED, READ... SAW SUNSHINE!
I CAN'T FIND MY EYEGLASSES!
DO A SEARCH FOR THEM ONLINE!
A DUNCE-A-SAURUS CLUB WANTS US TO BUILD A WEBSITE FOR THEM!
TELL THEM WE ALREADY DID... THEY WON'T KNOW THE DIFFERENCE!
I HATE BEING THE BOSS. I HAVE TO COME IN EARLY TO SEE WHO GETS IN LATE!
WHIRRRR!
ARE YOU CHATTING ON COMPANY TIME?
NO SIR...UH, JUST DOING RESEARCH!
MY COMPUTER IS ON A COFFEE BREAK!
COMPUTERS ARE WONDERFUL THINGS... AS LONG AS WE DON'T LET THEM RUN OUR LIVES!
I NEED MY OWN OFFICE!
KIDSBOOKS.COM
I HAVE EVERY SCREEN-SAVER EVER MADE!
BEEP-BEEP!

MULTI-CINEMA-SAURUS

FIND THESE ITEMS:

- ☐ "3"
- ☐ Backpack
- ☐ Balloon
- ☐ Bird
- ☐ Bowling bag
- ☐ Burned-out lightbulbs (4)
- ☐ Cane
- ☐ Cell phone
- ☐ Dollar bill
- ☐ Football helmet
- ☐ Gum
- ☐ Hearts (3)
- ☐ Ice-cream pop
- ☐ Lollipop
- ☐ Missing lightbulb
- ☐ Necktie
- ☐ Pillow
- ☐ Rollerskate
- ☐ Scooter
- ☐ Skier
- ☐ Straw
- ☐ Suspenders
- ☐ Toothbrush
- ☐ Top hat
- ☐ Turban
- ☐ Umbrella
- ☐ Volcano

MY NECK IS KILLING ME!
THAT'S THE LAST TIME WE SIT IN THE FRONT ROW.
I DEFINITELY MADE A WRONG TURN SOMEWHERE!
THIS IS THE PERFECT PLACE TO COME WHEN IT RAINS!
THEN LET'S COME BACK WHEN IT'S RAINING!
THE POPCORN COSTS AS MUCH AS THE MOVIE TICKET!
I LOVE A GOOD MOVIE!
THEN WHAT ARE YOU DOING HERE?
I'M LOST! WHICH THEATER ARE YOU IN AGAIN?
WHY ARE YOU SO TIRED?
DULL MOVIES WEAR ME OUT!
WHY DO THEY KEEP THE THEATERS DARK?
I GUESS THEY'RE TRYING TO CONSERVE ENERGY.
SOME OF THESE MOVIES ARE COMING OUT ON VIDEO NEXT WEEK!
I DON'T WANT TO SEE THAT MOVIE!
ARGUING WITH YOU IS LIKE TRYING TO BLOW OUT A LIGHTBULB!
I HOPE SHE DOESN'T SIT IN FRONT OF ME!
WHICH MOVIE DO YOU WANT TO SEE?
LET'S SPEND ALL DAY HERE AND SEE THEM ALL!
I'VE BEEN WAITING ON THIS LINE FOR SO LONG, I FORGOT WHAT MOVIE I CAME TO SEE!
I THOUGHT WE WERE GOING BOWLING!
WHY AM I HERE?
HOW CAN SO MANY GOOD ACTORS AND ACTRESSES MAKE SO MANY BAD MOVIES?
TOO BAD THEY DON'T HAVE MONEY BACK GUARANTEES ON MOVIES!

WELCOME TO THE TRIVIA-SAURUS CONVENTION

FIND THESE ITEMS:

- ☐ Astronaut
- ☐ Automobile
- ☐ Banana peel
- ☐ Baseball cap
- ☐ Book
- ☐ Candle
- ☐ Candy cane
- ☐ Cup
- ☐ Eyeglasses
- ☐ Feather
- ☐ Flower
- ☐ Flying bat
- ☐ Ghost
- ☐ Hearts (4)
- ☐ Ice-cream pop
- ☐ Ice skates
- ☐ Jack-o'-lantern
- ☐ Keys (2)
- ☐ Necktie
- ☐ Pencil
- ☐ Pizza delivery dino
- ☐ Pointy beard
- ☐ Propeller
- ☐ Purse
- ☐ Rabbit
- ☐ Rollerskate
- ☐ Scarf
- ☐ Sunglasses
- ☐ Volcano
- ☐ Yo-yo

I DON'T KNOW THE ANSWERS TO ANY OF THESE TRIVIAS!
AM I LATE FOR THIS CONVENTION?
IS THAT A MULTIPLE CHOICE TRIVIA QUESTION?
ARE YOU THINKING WHAT I'M THINKING?
THERE'S A SCARY THOUGHT!
TRIVIA TREAT
WHAT'S OUR MOTTO?
IF YOU DON'T ASK, YOU'LL NEVER KNOW!
HOW DID I END UP HERE?
YOU CHARGE $5.00 FOR ANSWERING TWO QUESTIONS?
THAT IS CORRECT! SECOND QUESTION, PLEASE!
TOO MANY!
HOW MANY DINOSAURS ATTEND THIS CONVENTION EVERY YEAR?
I HAVE MORE QUESTIONS THAN ANSWERS!
I'M ON A QUEST FOR CORRECT ANSWERS!
SO WHY COME HERE?
WHY DO THEY CALL THEM **JUMBO** SHRIMP?
CURIOSITY KILLED THE CAT!
WHAT WAS SO IMPORTANT THAT THE CAT HAD TO KNOW?
DID YOU EVER SEE A SCHOOL SPIRIT?
WHY ARE DINOSAURS SO POPULAR?
WHO GETS THE PIZZA?
WHY IS ABBREVIATED SUCH A LONG WORD?
BECAUSE WE'RE CUTE!
I CAN'T BELIEVE I PAID AN ADMISSION TO GET INTO THIS CONVENTION!

LUNCH ROOM-A-SAURUS

FIND THESE ITEMS:

- ☐ Alien
- ☐ Backpack
- ☐ Banana peel
- ☐ Bones (2)
- ☐ Broken heart
- ☐ Broom
- ☐ Candle
- ☐ Cell phone
- ☐ Cook
- ☐ Dino ordering pizza
- ☐ Fire hydrant
- ☐ Fish
- ☐ Football helmet
- ☐ Guitar
- ☐ Hammer
- ☐ Ice-cream cone
- ☐ Music note
- ☐ Napkin dispenser
- ☐ Necktie
- ☐ Old tire
- ☐ Paper airplane
- ☐ Pencils (3)
- ☐ Periscope
- ☐ Roller skate
- ☐ Santa cap
- ☐ Skateboard
- ☐ Sock
- ☐ Umbrella
- ☐ Worm

WHEN I GROW UP I WANT TO BE A HEALTH INSPECTOR!
GREAT, THEN YOU CAN CLOSE THIS PLACE DOWN!
I WISH I COULD COOK!
YOU'RE LUCKY YOU KNOW HOW TO MAKE ICE.
IS THIS THE LUNCH ROOM?
NO, THIS IS THE PRINCIPAL'S OFFICE...WE ALL HAVE DETENTION!
IT'S ALIVE!
I'M NOT COMING OUT UNTIL THEY LEAVE!
IF YOU HAD EIGHT SLICES OF PIZZA AND ATE SIX... WHAT WOULD YOU HAVE?
A STOMACH-ACHE!
WHY ARE YOU WHISPERING?
THIS CORN HAS EARS!
NOW THAT I'VE SEEN TODAY'S MENU, I THINK I'LL GO ON A DIET.
I LIKE THE FOOD HERE!
THERE'S NO ACCOUNTING FOR TASTE!
I'M NOT EATING HERE!
IT'S STUCK!
WHY ARE YOU WEARING YOUR HELMET?
I WANT TO ORDER A PEPPERONI PIZZA.
MY BROTHER IS WEIRD... HE HAS COLD PIZZA AND MILK FOR BREAKFAST.
THAT IS WEIRD... I USUALLY DRINK LEMON JUICE WITH MINE.
I DIDN'T KNOW IT WAS POSSIBLE TO FAIL LUNCH!
THE SOUP IS A LITTLE HEAVY TODAY!
THE FOOD HERE IS PRETTY BAD! YESTERDAY I CRACKED A TOOTH ON THE GRAVY!
I WANT TO GO HOME FOR LUNCH!
I KNOW!
WHAT IS BACTERIA?
THE REAR ENTRANCE TO THE CAFETERIA.
THIS PLACE NEEDS TABLE SERVICE.
ICU

FARM-A-SAURUS

FIND THESE ITEMS:

- ☐ Axe
- ☐ Balloon
- ☐ Candy cane
- ☐ Coffeepot
- ☐ Cow
- ☐ Crayons (3)
- ☐ Crows (7)
- ☐ Dog
- ☐ Duck
- ☐ Empty flowerpot
- ☐ Golf ball
- ☐ Golf club
- ☐ Hoe
- ☐ Horseshoe
- ☐ Ice-cream cone
- ☐ Key
- ☐ Kite
- ☐ Mouse
- ☐ Neckerchief
- ☐ Pear
- ☐ Pencil
- ☐ Pitchfork
- ☐ Rooster
- ☐ Shovel
- ☐ Snake
- ☐ Star
- ☐ Tic-tac-toe
- ☐ Tires (7)
- ☐ Toothbrush
- ☐ Top hat
- ☐ Turtle
- ☐ Watering can
- ☐ Wristwatch

DO THE ANIMALS EVER GET A VACATION?
YES, ONCE A YEAR WE SEND THEM TO DINO LAND.
THIS IS A SPAGHETTI TREE?
YEP, JUST ABOUT READY TO HARVEST!
WHY WERE YOU DANCING WITH A COW LAST NIGHT?
I WANTED A MILKSHAKE!
HOW MANY SHEEP DOES IT TAKE TO MAKE ONE SWEATER?
I DIDN'T KNOW SHEEP COULD KNIT SWEATERS!
I'M THE WORLD'S BIGGEST SCARECROW!
WHO ARE YOU SUPPOSED TO SCARE AWAY?
3 WISHES 10¢
HONK!
A CRAYON FARM?
?
?
I GET UP EVERY MORNING AT 5:30 REGARDLESS OF WHAT TIME IT IS.
YAWN!
THESE TOMATOES LOOK WEIRD!
THAT'S BECAUSE THEY'RE ONIONS!
FORE!

SKATEBOARD-A-SAURUS

FIND THESE ITEMS:

- ☐ Auto
- ☐ Band-aid
- ☐ Banana peel
- ☐ Baseball cap
- ☐ Broken heart
- ☐ Cactus
- ☐ Doghouse
- ☐ Fish (2)
- ☐ Flashlight
- ☐ Ghost
- ☐ Hammer
- ☐ Helmet
- ☐ Lost shoe
- ☐ Motorized board
- ☐ Mushroom
- ☐ Pencil
- ☐ Periscope
- ☐ Pie
- ☐ Pizza
- ☐ Pogo stick
- ☐ Ring
- ☐ Scarf
- ☐ Shark fin
- ☐ Sled
- ☐ Star
- ☐ Three-wheeled board
- ☐ Top hat
- ☐ Turtle
- ☐ Winged board
- ☐ Yo-yo

THAT'S WEIRD!
NOW THIS PLACE IS PIZZA-TO-GO!
THIS ISN'T AS EASY AS IT LOOKS!
THIS IS THE WAY TO GO!
HAS ANYONE SEEN MY BOARD?
THIS PARK NEEDS A FIRST AID STATION!
NOW I SEE WHY IT'S IMPORTANT TO WEAR A HELMET!
THIS COURSE IS TOUGH!
THIS PLACE IS SO EXCITING!
I THINK I'LL REMOVE THE WHEELS AND TAKE THIS TO THE OCEAN!
?
DO NOT TRY THIS!!
WE USE ONLY PROFESSIONAL SKATEBOARDERS!!

ROBOTIC-A-SAURUS

FIND THESE ITEMS:

- ☐ Arrow
- ☐ Balloon
- ☐ Banana peel
- ☐ Bow tie
- ☐ Brush
- ☐ Crystal ball
- ☐ Fire hydrant
- ☐ Hammer
- ☐ Hearts (2)
- ☐ Ice-cream cone
- ☐ Ice skates
- ☐ Kite
- ☐ Light bulbs (2)
- ☐ Loose screw
- ☐ Necktie
- ☐ Oil can
- ☐ Pencils (2)
- ☐ Pizza
- ☐ Roller skates
- ☐ Satellite dish
- ☐ Shoulder bag
- ☐ Star
- ☐ Sunglasses
- ☐ Telescope
- ☐ Umbrella
- ☐ Vacuum
- ☐ Yo-yo

ARE YOU PROGRAMMED TO TAKE OUT THE TRASH CANS?
UNFORTUNATELY, YES!
WHERE IS THE WIND-UP KEY?
I COULD USE SOME OIL!
TWO QUARTS?
ME, TOO!
AS SOON AS I'M ASKED TO DO WORK... I SHUT DOWN!
I HOPE SOME-BODY NICE WILL BUY ME!
MY EYES GLOW IN THE DARK!
ULP!
ISN'T TECHNOLOGY WONDERFUL...WONDERFUL... WONDERFUL...WONDERFUL... WONDERFUL...WONDER...
I HAVE 300 MILES OF ELECTRICAL CABLE IN MY TAIL ALONE!
I'M PROGRAMMED TO DELIVER PIZZA!
I CAN PREDICT THE WEATHER!
MY BACK-UP SYSTEM NEEDS A BACK-UP SYSTEM!
WHERE HAVE YOU BEEN ALL MY LIFE?
I'M PROGRAMMED TO LOOK COOL!

SO YOU WANT TO BE A **STAR-A-SAURUS**

FIND THESE ITEMS:

- ☐ Beret
- ☐ Bird
- ☐ Bottle
- ☐ Bow ties (2)
- ☐ Box
- ☐ Candle
- ☐ Clipboard
- ☐ Crown
- ☐ Dracula-saurus
- ☐ Drum
- ☐ Flower
- ☐ Fork
- ☐ Frying pan
- ☐ Ghost
- ☐ Heart
- ☐ Medal
- ☐ Mustaches (2)
- ☐ Pearl necklace
- ☐ Pencils (2)
- ☐ Periscope
- ☐ Pointy beards (2)
- ☐ Scarves (3)
- ☐ Stars (2)
- ☐ Sunglasses (3)
- ☐ Sword
- ☐ Ten-gallon hat
- ☐ Ticket
- ☐ Tic-tac-toe
- ☐ Top hat
- ☐ Walking stick

I'M HERE TO READ FOR THE PART OF THE MASTER CHEF.
IS THIS WHERE THE CIRCUS IS AUDITIONING CLOWNS?
THIS IS A COMEDY SHOW?
IF YOU NEED A COWPOKE TO LASSO A STEER... I'M THE ONE!
WHEN DOES THE VIDEO VERSION OF THIS SHOW GET RELEASED?
I THOUGHT IT WAS A HOLLOWEEN SHOW!
I'M GOING TO NEED A SPOTLIGHT!
I'M A NATURAL SINGER.
YES, YOUR TONGUE IS SHARP AND YOUR FEET ARE FLAT!
I WANT TO SEE MY NAME IN LIGHTS!
TO BE OR NOT TO BE...
CHANGE YOUR NAME TO "60 WATTS" THEN!
I'M AUDITIONING FOR THE PART OF THE DIRECTOR!
THIS SHOW IS A FLOP-A-SAURUS!
CAN YOU GIVE ME STAGE DIRECTIONS?
SURE! THE EXIT IS THAT WAY!

MARATHON-A-SAURUS

FIND THESE ITEMS:

- ☐ Automobile
- ☐ Axe
- ☐ Bird
- ☐ Bowling ball
- ☐ Cactus
- ☐ Cell phone
- ☐ Coffeepot
- ☐ Cup
- ☐ Fire hydrant
- ☐ Fish
- ☐ Jack-o'-lantern
- ☐ Jester's cap
- ☐ Key
- ☐ Kite
- ☐ Lost baseball caps (2)
- ☐ Moustache
- ☐ Pencil
- ☐ Rolling pin
- ☐ Skateboard
- ☐ Socks (2)
- ☐ Star
- ☐ Straw
- ☐ Telescope
- ☐ Tent
- ☐ Traffic light
- ☐ Tulip
- ☐ Turtle
- ☐ Volcano

WHAT BOTHERS ME ABOUT MARATHONS IS THE RUNNING!
HEY, YOU'RE ON THE WRONG PAGE!
I KNOW!
HOW MUCH FURTHER IS IT?
WE JUST STARTED!
WHO ARE YOU CALLING?
A TAXI!
WHERE'S THE PIZZA DELIVERY DINO WHEN YOU NEED HIM?
FOLLOW ME! I KNOW A SHORTCUT!
DO DROP IN!
WATCH YOUR STEP
NOW WOULD BE A GOOD TIME TO TELL THEM THAT THEY'RE RUNNING THE WRONG WAY!
THE ONLY WAY I WOULD RUN IN THIS RACE IS IF I KNEW THERE WAS A BUFFET AT THE END OF IT!
MY FEET HURT FROM JUST WATCHING!
I USUALLY ONLY RUN LIKE THIS WHEN I HEAR THAT DINNER'S BEING SERVED!
WHAT DOES THE WINNER WIN?
A FOOT MASSAGE, I HOPE!
I'M IN THE LEAD BY A HORN!
I HOPE WE PASS A TACO STAND.
I'M NUMBER TWO!

HARD HAT-A-SAURUS

FIND THESE ITEMS:

- ☐ Arrows (5)
- ☐ Astronaut
- ☐ Balloons (3)
- ☐ Banana peel
- ☐ Bicycle
- ☐ Book
- ☐ Bowling ball
- ☐ Clothes line
- ☐ Comb
- ☐ Cow
- ☐ Fish
- ☐ Fish bowl
- ☐ Football
- ☐ Hearts (2)
- ☐ Igloo
- ☐ Lunchbox
- ☐ Moose head
- ☐ Mouse
- ☐ Paint can
- ☐ Sail
- ☐ Saw
- ☐ Scarf
- ☐ Snake
- ☐ Socks (2)
- ☐ Sunglasses
- ☐ Tepee
- ☐ Thermometer
- ☐ Top hat
- ☐ Turtle
- ☐ Used tire
- ☐ Wheelbarrow

EATS
EATS
WHO ORDERED PIZZA?
WHAT ARE THESE DINOS DOING UP HERE?
DID YOU PACK A LUNCH?
NO, I'M HAVING A HOT-AIR BALLOON DROP ONE DOWN!
THIS WAS ONCE A QUIET SKY!
HOLD THE MAYO ON THAT... RIGHT?
HENRY! YOU FORGOT YOUR HANKY!
WHAT ARE WE BUILDING, ANYWAY?
YOU MEAN YOU DON'T KNOW, EITHER?
LET'S PLAY TOUCH FOOTBALL!
WHATEVER YOU GUYS DO... DON'T STAND BACK AND ADMIRE YOUR WORK!
MY HOROSCOPE SAYS THAT I'M GOING ON A SURPRISE TRIP!
ARE WE GOING TO WELD THESE BEAMS TOGETHER?
NO, I THOUGHT WE'D USE DUCT TAPE!
THIS CONSTRUCTION SITE SHOULD HAVE ITS OWN WEBSITE!
YOU WERE AFRAID OF THE HEIGHTS?
YES, BUT NOW I'M ONLY AFRAID OF WIDTHS!
LET'S CALL IT A DAY!
SURE! WHICH ONE?

THE FAMOUS STORY OF
FRANKENSAURUS

FIND THESE ITEMS:

- ☐ Alarm clock
- ☐ Axe
- ☐ Banana peel
- ☐ Band-aids (2)
- ☐ Baseball bat
- ☐ Baseball cap
- ☐ Bow and arrow
- ☐ Bowling ball
- ☐ Candle
- ☐ Cupcake
- ☐ Dead flower
- ☐ Drum
- ☐ Eyeglasses
- ☐ Fire hydrant
- ☐ Fish
- ☐ Football
- ☐ Heart
- ☐ Knitting needles
- ☐ Lollipop
- ☐ Oil can
- ☐ Paddle
- ☐ Paper airplane
- ☐ Pencils (2)
- ☐ Periscope
- ☐ Pizza
- ☐ Rolling pin
- ☐ Saw
- ☐ Scissors
- ☐ Screwdriver
- ☐ Sunglasses
- ☐ Tape
- ☐ Thermometer
- ☐ Tic-tac-toe
- ☐ Turtle
- ☐ Yo-yo

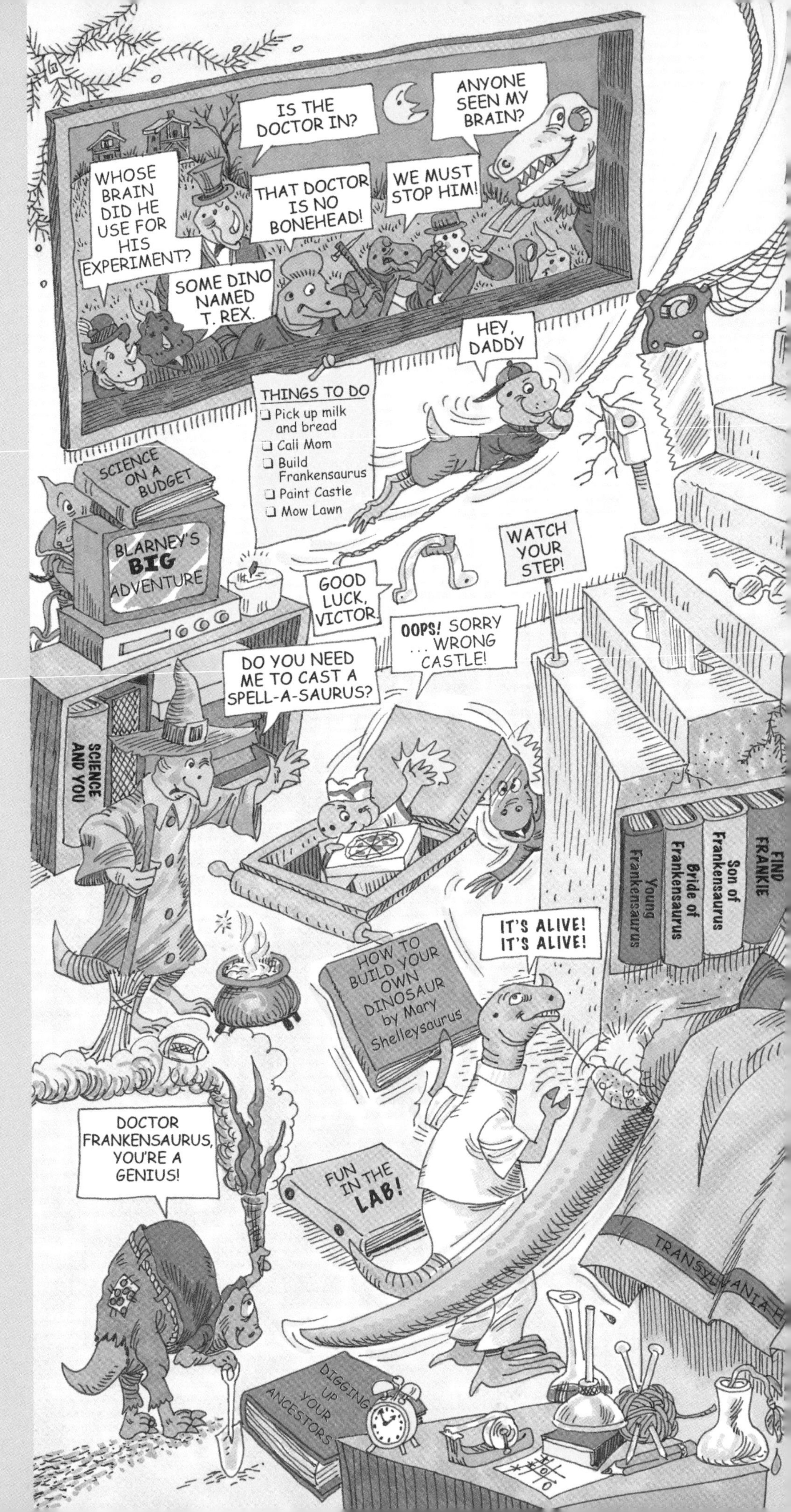

LUNCH IS SERVED!
AH . . . WE HAVE A GUEST FOR LUNCH!
I'M GERTIE, THE DOCTOR'S WIFE!
GET ALL THE TOWN'S DINOS HERE!
DOES HE MAKE HOUSE CALLS?
WE'RE TOO LATE!
BURP! EXCUSE ME!
ULP! WHERE AM I . . . IS THIS THE LOST WORLD?
THIS IS SOME TALL-TALE!
BORIS KARLOFF FAN CLUB
I'VE BEEN IN HIS WAITING ROOM FOR FIVE HOURS!
SQUEAK!
I'M STAYING HERE!
DOES HE DO FACE-LIFTS?
THIS END UP
I'M MUMMY-SAURUS.
?
THIS PLACE GIVES ME THE CREEPS!
PRESERVATIVE
NO ARTIFICIAL COLORING
101 FUN EXPERIMENTS
RENOVATING YOUR CASTLE
HOW TO SEW
EXTRA PARTS
DO NOT REMOVE
HOME SWEET HOME
RIP!
DOES HE LIKE CHEESE?

DINO-WRESTLING IS REALLY HUGE!

FIND THESE ITEMS:

- ☐ Band-Aid
- ☐ Baseball caps (3)
- ☐ Baseball glove
- ☐ Basketball
- ☐ Bow tie
- ☐ Camera
- ☐ Drinking straw
- ☐ Egg
- ☐ Envelope
- ☐ Flowers
- ☐ Harmonica
- ☐ Headphones (2)
- ☐ Heart
- ☐ Hot dog
- ☐ Ice-cream cone
- ☐ Kite
- ☐ Lost balloons (2)
- ☐ Microphone
- ☐ Necktie
- ☐ Pencils (2)
- ☐ Periscope
- ☐ Scarf
- ☐ Slice of pizza
- ☐ Straw hat
- ☐ Sunglasses
- ☐ Telescope
- ☐ Top hat
- ☐ Yo-yo

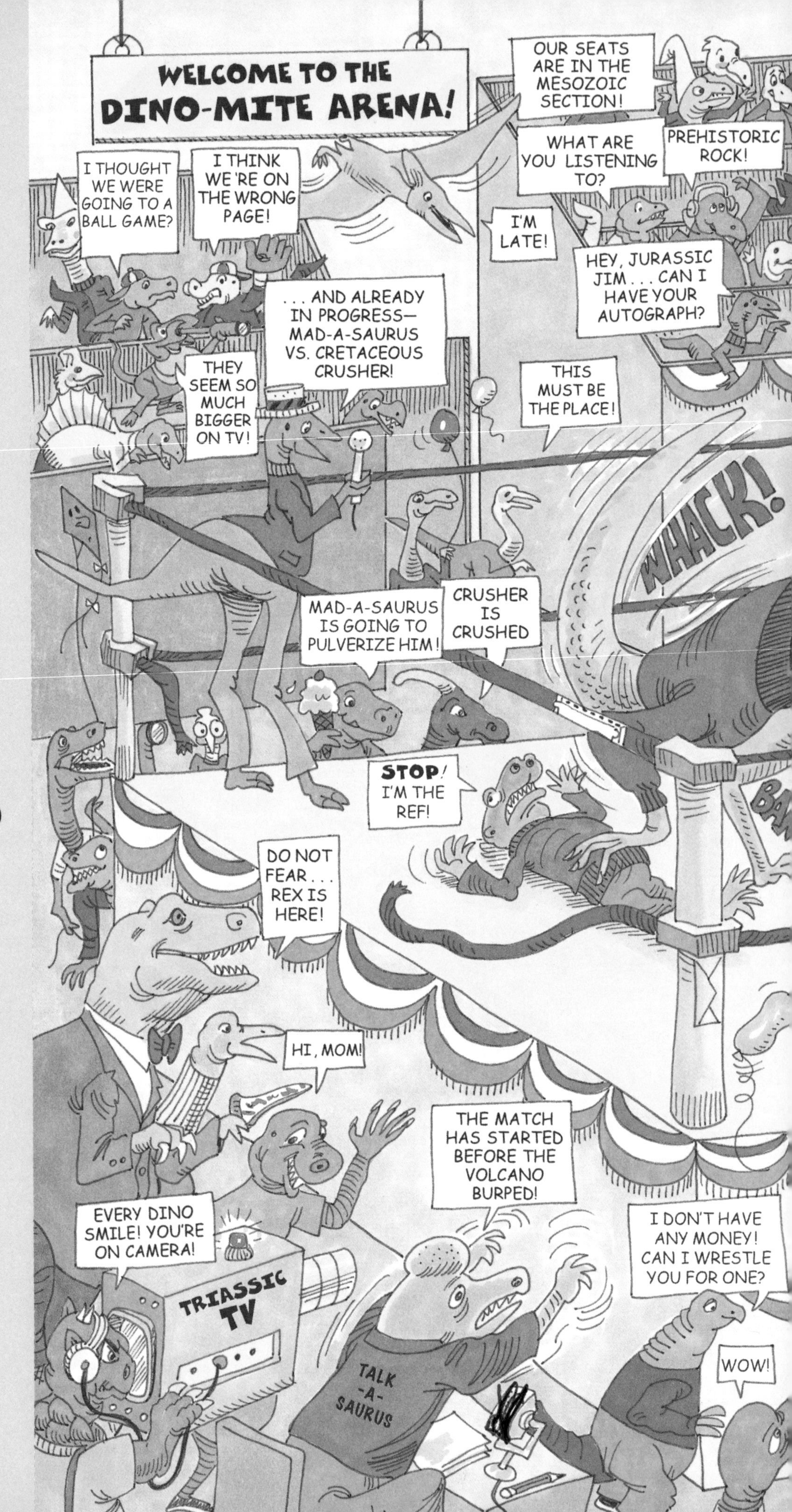

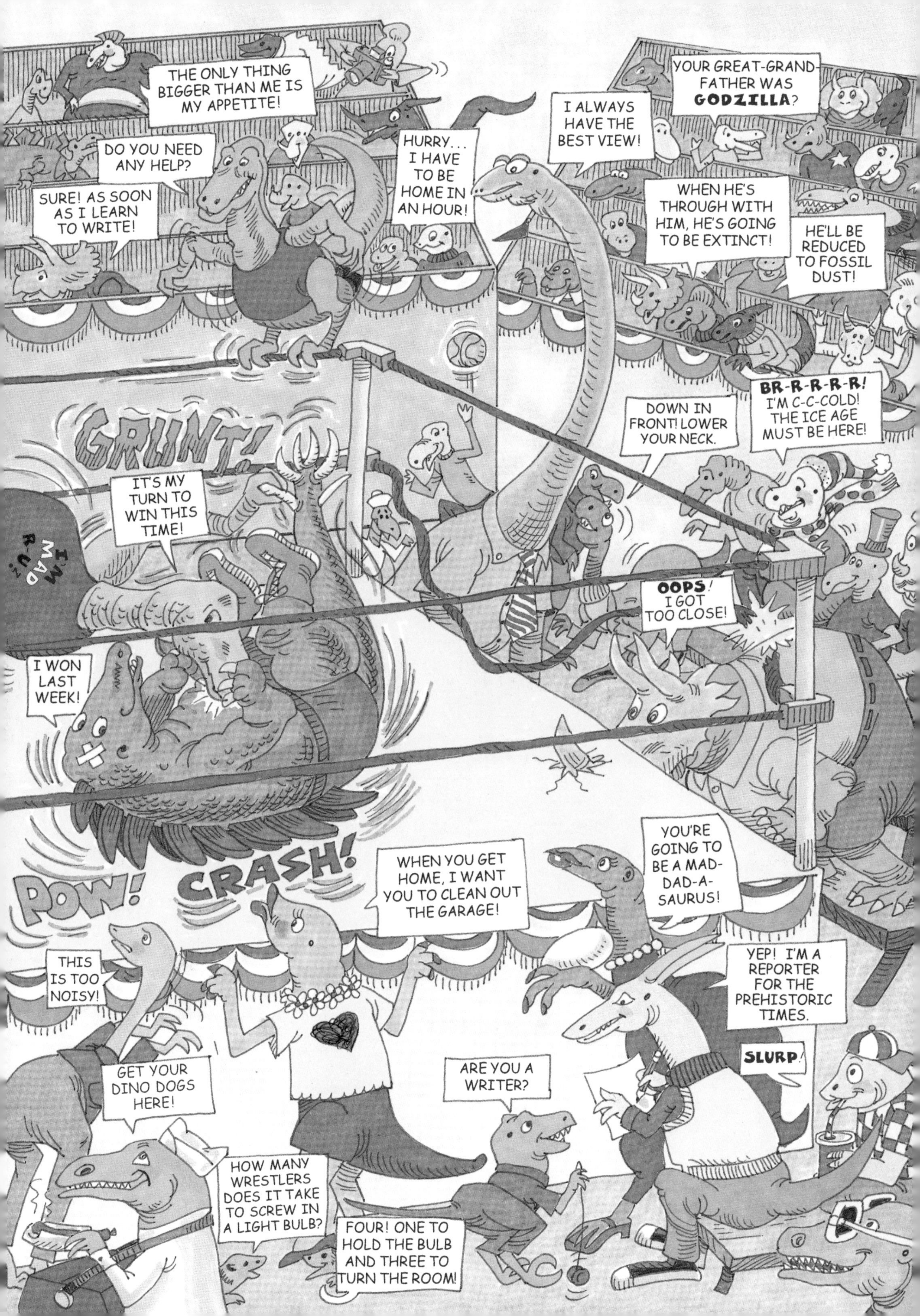
THE ONLY THING BIGGER THAN ME IS MY APPETITE!
DO YOU NEED ANY HELP?
SURE! AS SOON AS I LEARN TO WRITE!
HURRY... I HAVE TO BE HOME IN AN HOUR!
I ALWAYS HAVE THE BEST VIEW!
YOUR GREAT-GRAND-FATHER WAS GODZILLA?
WHEN HE'S THROUGH WITH HIM, HE'S GOING TO BE EXTINCT!
HE'LL BE REDUCED TO FOSSIL DUST!
GRUNT!
DOWN IN FRONT! LOWER YOUR NECK.
BR-R-R-R-R! I'M C-C-COLD! THE ICE AGE MUST BE HERE!
IT'S MY TURN TO WIN THIS TIME!
I'M MAD R-U?
OOPS! I GOT TOO CLOSE!
I WON LAST WEEK!
POW!
CRASH!
WHEN YOU GET HOME, I WANT YOU TO CLEAN OUT THE GARAGE!
YOU'RE GOING TO BE A MAD-DAD-A-SAURUS!
THIS IS TOO NOISY!
YEP! I'M A REPORTER FOR THE PREHISTORIC TIMES.
SLURP!
GET YOUR DINO DOGS HERE!
ARE YOU A WRITER?
HOW MANY WRESTLERS DOES IT TAKE TO SCREW IN A LIGHT BULB?
FOUR! ONE TO HOLD THE BULB AND THREE TO TURN THE ROOM!

THE VOYAGE OF CHRISTOPHER COLUMBUSAURUS

FIND THESE ITEMS:

- ☐ Balloons (3)
- ☐ Barber pole
- ☐ Bird
- ☐ Brushes (2)
- ☐ Bullhorn
- ☐ Candle
- ☐ Chef's hat
- ☐ Fire hydrant
- ☐ Fishing rod
- ☐ Heart
- ☐ Horseshoe
- ☐ Hourglass
- ☐ Ice-cream cone
- ☐ Key
- ☐ Kite
- ☐ Mermaid
- ☐ Periscope
- ☐ Pie
- ☐ Sock
- ☐ Sunglasses
- ☐ Sailor's cap
- ☐ Telescope
- ☐ Tire
- ☐ Umbrella
- ☐ Yo-yo

THIS IS THE LONGEST 7-DAY CRUISE I'VE EVER BEEN ON! WE'VE BEEN AT SEA FOR MONTHS!
TIME FLIES WHEN YOU'RE SEASICK!
THEY STOPPED FOR GAS!
HEY, ARE YOU GUYS LOST?
PLEASE DO NOT DISEMBARK UNTIL THE SHIP HAS COME TO A COMPLETE STOP!
THANK YOU FOR SAILING ABOARD THE SANTA MARIASAURUS!
I GUESS THE WORLD ISN'T FLAT AFTER ALL.
I HOPE THE NEW WORLD HAS SOUVENIR SHOPS.
SOMEWHERE AROUND HERE!
WHAT ARE OUR COORDINATES?
I LOVE SEAFOOD... ESPECIALLY SALT WATER TAFFY.
HOW CAN I KEEP THIS SHIP LOOKING BEAUTIFUL?
I HOPE THEY DIDN'T LOSE MY LUGGAGE AGAIN!
HEY, CHRIS, IS THAT THE WEST INDIES?
JUMP OVER-BOARD.
ARE WE THERE YET?
I CAN'T TELL! I'VE GOT THIS THING STUCK IN MY EYE!
TODAY IS: OCT. 12, 1492
WHAT'S FOR DINNER?
IT COULD BE A NEW LAND CALLED AMERICA.
YOU READ TOO MANY BOOKS.
HI, GUYS!
I'VE BEEN HERE BEFORE.
THIS IS THE LIFE!
DIVE! DIVE!

DINOSAURS IN SPACE

FIND THESE ITEMS:

- ☐ Apple
- ☐ Banana
- ☐ Band-Aid
- ☐ Barber pole
- ☐ Baseball
- ☐ Baseball cap
- ☐ Bow tie
- ☐ Cane
- ☐ Carrot
- ☐ Coffeepot
- ☐ Cups (2)
- ☐ Envelopes (2)
- ☐ Flower pot
- ☐ Garden hose
- ☐ Hammer
- ☐ Hitchhiker
- ☐ Ice-cream cone
- ☐ Key
- ☐ Kite
- ☐ Lost shoe
- ☐ Medal
- ☐ Oil can
- ☐ Pencil
- ☐ Saw
- ☐ Screwdriver
- ☐ Shovel
- ☐ Speaker
- ☐ Telescope
- ☐ Tepee
- ☐ Tic-tac-toe
- ☐ Toothbrush

PLANET OF THE DINO
NEED RIDE TO EARTH.
OOPS! I LEFT THE DOOR OPEN!
WHY DID YOU BRING SO MUCH MONEY?
ILLEGALLY PARKED SPACECRAFTS WILL BE TOWED AT OWNERS' EXPENSE.
I HEARD THE MOON MAY BE DOWN TO ITS LAST QUARTER!
DO NOT OPEN
WINDOWS
I DON'T WANT YOU GUYS ARGUING ABOUT WHO GETS THE WINDOW SEAT ON THE WAY HOME!
WE'RE NEVER GOING TO FIND A PARKING SPOT!
MY BROTHER WAS FIRED FROM THE SPACE PROGRAM. HE INSISTED ON RIDING WITH THE TOP DOWN DURING LIFT-OFF!
IT'S A FLYING SAUCER!
NO! IT'S THE PEPPERONI PIZZA WE ORDERED!
LET ME IN!
DO WE MAKE A LEFT OR A RIGHT AT JUPITER?
LET'S WATCH THE DRYOSAURUS CHANNEL.
HI, MOM!
THAT DEPENDS. DO WE WANT TO TAKE THE SCENIC ROUTE?
ANYONE HAVE SPARE CHANGE FOR THE TOLL?
WHY WERE YOU SO NERVOUS AT BLAST-OFF?
I SAW THE CREW BRINGING OUT JUMPER CABLES!
DID SOMEONE SAY PIZZA?

DINO VACATIONS IN NEW YORK CITY

FIND THESE ITEMS:

- ☐ Banana
- ☐ Bicycle messenger
- ☐ Bone
- ☐ Burned-out bulbs (3)
- ☐ Camera
- ☐ Cane
- ☐ Clipboard
- ☐ Clothespin
- ☐ Crayon
- ☐ Envelope
- ☐ Fire hydrants (3)
- ☐ Fork
- ☐ Ghost
- ☐ Hearts (2)
- ☐ Horseshoe
- ☐ Ice-cream cone
- ☐ In-line skater
- ☐ Jack-o'-lantern
- ☐ Ladder
- ☐ Lost balloon
- ☐ Mouse
- ☐ Paintbrush
- ☐ Paper airplane
- ☐ Party hat
- ☐ Tepee
- ☐ Worm

NOW PLAYING
BEAUTY AND THE BRACHIOSAURUS
BLARNEY
LIVE ON STAGE
IT'S A GOOD THING THAT WE AREN'T AFRAID OF HEIGHTS!
WHAT DO YOU MEAN WE?
THE CRETACEOUS INN
LIZARD LOUNGE
DID YOU REALLY DESIGN THE COLORS ON THAT NECKTIE YOU'RE WEARING?
YES, I LEANED OVER SOME OPEN CANS OF PAINT!
DINO-MAIL
I'M LEFT OVER FROM THE THANKSGIVING DAY PARADE!
HI, EVERYBODY. WE'RE IN THE HEART OF TIMES SQUAREASAURUS.
HAPPY NEW YEAR!
EVERYBODY SMILE!
DON'T LOOK UP! THEY'LL KNOW WE'RE FROM OUT OF TOWN!
NEED MONEY FOR MUSIC LESSONS.
DINO-LIVERY
WHICH ONE IS THE PREHISTORIC TIMES BUILDING?
WHICH WAY?
REX-CAB
WHAT IS THIS LINE FOR?
I DON'T KNOW! BUT IT'S NOT TOO LONG.
HONK-HONK-HONK!
HOW DO I GET TO CARNEGIE HALLASAURUS?
HONK! HONK! BEEP! HONK!
MIDTOWN
PRACTICE
WHICH IS THE BUILDING KING KONG CLIMBED?
BEEP!
DO YOU WANT TO FIND THE STATUE OF LIBERTY?
I DIDN'T KNOW SHE WAS MISSING!
BEEP! HONK!
SKREECH!
HONK! BEEP!
ROAR!

DINOSAURS IN
KING ARTHUR'S COURT

FIND THESE ITEMS:

- ☐ Balloon
- ☐ Banana
- ☐ Banana peels (2)
- ☐ Baseball cap
- ☐ Basketball
- ☐ Bell
- ☐ Bird
- ☐ Bone
- ☐ Bow tie
- ☐ Candle
- ☐ Carrot
- ☐ Clothespins (3)
- ☐ Earring
- ☐ Feather
- ☐ Ice-cream cone
- ☐ Jestersaurus
- ☐ Jugglesaurus
- ☐ Light bulb
- ☐ Merlinasaurus
- ☐ Pearl necklace
- ☐ Roller skate
- ☐ Sock
- ☐ Swords (3)
- ☐ Telescope
- ☐ Whale

I CAN'T MOVE! I GOT CAUGHT IN THE RAIN!
SQUEAK!
SQUEAK!
I'M LOOKING FOR A DAMSEL IN DISTRESS.
THE KING ENCOURAGES ME TO SAY WHAT I THINK!
AS LONG AS YOU AGREE WITH HIM!
I'M THINKING OF OPENING MY OWN CASTLE!
IT'S A GREAT DAY TO BE A KNIGHT.
THIS CASTLE HAS A VERY MEDIEVAL FEELING TO IT!
I THINK IT FEELS DRAFTY.
KEEP OUR CASTLE CLEAN!
PROPERTY OF KING ARTHURSAURUS
NAPOLEONASAURUS
WHEE-E-E-E!
I'M FROM CAMELOT PIZZA... WHO ORDERED A PIE?
HOW ARE WE GOING TO GET THIS OUT?
I ESCAPED FROM THE DUNGEON!
ROBIN HOOD WAS HERE!
WHY DOESN'T ANYONE EVER RECOGNIZE ME?
IF THIS WAS MY CASTLE, I'D PUT IN AN ELEVATOR.
THE DRAWBRIDGE WAS UP...I HAD TO SWIM THE MOAT!
ONE WAY
WHO IS THAT?
THAT'S LADY GUINEVEREASAURUS... THE KING'S WIFE.
ARE YOU KNIGHTS GREAT AND NOBLE?
I'M GREAT! HE'S NOBLE!

DINO SUPERHEROES

FIND THESE ITEMS:

- ☐ Arrow
- ☐ Banana peel
- ☐ Bone
- ☐ Cactus
- ☐ Chef's hat
- ☐ Drum
- ☐ Envelope
- ☐ Fish
- ☐ Football
- ☐ Gavel
- ☐ Hammer
- ☐ Heart
- ☐ Hot dog
- ☐ Jack-o'-lantern
- ☐ Key
- ☐ Kite
- ☐ Owl
- ☐ Paper airplane
- ☐ Pencil
- ☐ Rabbit
- ☐ Screwdriver
- ☐ Seal
- ☐ Straw
- ☐ Tack
- ☐ Television
- ☐ Toothbrush
- ☐ Umbrella

I'M A VERY VERSATILE SUPERHERO!
YES, YOU DO EVERYTHING WRONG!
I'M HAVING AN AMUSEMENT PARK NAMED AFTER ME!
WHO MADE YOUR COSTUME?
MY MOM.
OH!... I MISPLACED MY UTILITY BELT AGAIN!
I ONCE FORGOT TO PUT ON MY CAPE!
NO ONE EVER ASKS ME FOR MY AUTOGRAPH!
THAT WORKS OUT VERY WELL... SINCE YOU CAN'T WRITE!
IGUANADON COMICS
WHAT WERE YOU LIKE AS A BABY?
VERY SHORT
LOOK, EVERYBODY! I HAVE MY OWN COMIC BOOK!
WHAT'S YOUR SUPER-SAURUS POWER?
EATING!
I KNOW, YESTERDAY SOME KID LAUGHED AT MY COSTUME!
MY FAMILY TELLS ME I'M AN EMBARRASSMENT.
WHO'S READY FOR A SNACK?

WILD WEST TOWN

FIND THESE ITEMS:

- ☐ Arrows (2)
- ☐ Axe
- ☐ Badges (2)
- ☐ Balloons (2)
- ☐ Banana
- ☐ Barrel
- ☐ Bones (2)
- ☐ Bow tie
- ☐ Brush
- ☐ Cactus (2)
- ☐ Candle
- ☐ Cheese
- ☐ Coonskin caps (2)
- ☐ Cup
- ☐ Drums (2)
- ☐ Elephant
- ☐ Eyeglasses
- ☐ Fire hydrant
- ☐ Fish
- ☐ Flower
- ☐ Football
- ☐ Heart
- ☐ Horseshoe
- ☐ Pencil
- ☐ Razor
- ☐ Ring
- ☐ Top hat
- ☐ Worm

NOT OK CORRAL
5 MILES
GRAND CANYONASAURUS
10 MILES
THIS MUST BE THE PLACE!
ARBER-AURUS
...AND CLOSE SHAVES
JAIL-ASAURUS
ALL WELCOME
THE FOSSIL INN
ANKYLOSAUR
FAST FOOD GRI
ALL YOU CAN EAT!
THERE'S NOTHING WILD ABOUT THIS TOWN!
I'VE SEEN MORE EXCITEMENT AT A TORTOISE RACE!
WHY DID YOU GROW A MOUSTACHE AND BEARD?
SO I WOULDN'T HAVE TO BUY SHAVING CREAM!
I GUESS YOU'RE THE SHERIFF'S DEPUTY?
NO, I GOT THIS BADGE IN A CEREAL BOX!
WHO PLANTS TUMBLE-WEED?
I LIKE WATCHING THE TUMBLING TUMBLE-WEED!
MY THROAT HURTS WHEN I SING.
MY EARS HURT WHEN YOU SING!
WHAT BROUGHT YOU OUT WEST?
MY REAR TWO LEGS!
TONTO... WHERE ARE YOU?
WHO WEARS THE BIGGEST HAT IN TOWN?
THE DINOSAUR WITH THE BIGGEST HEAD!

PICNIC-A-SAURUS

FIND THESE ITEMS:

- ☐ Arrow
- ☐ Baseball caps (2)
- ☐ Bone
- ☐ Cactus
- ☐ Comb
- ☐ Cell phone
- ☐ Eyeglasses (2)
- ☐ Fish
- ☐ Flower
- ☐ Football
- ☐ Forks (3)
- ☐ Four-leaf clover
- ☐ Frog
- ☐ Ghost
- ☐ Hot dog
- ☐ Lamp
- ☐ Lion
- ☐ Lost kite
- ☐ Lost sunglasses
- ☐ Mushroom
- ☐ Pie
- ☐ Pizza delivery dino
- ☐ Propeller
- ☐ Ring
- ☐ Salt shaker
- ☐ Star
- ☐ Yo-yo

THINK IT WILL RAIN?
NOW THAT WE'RE ALL SET UP, I'M SURE IT WILL.
KEEP OFF THE GRASS
SHH..!
WATERMELON IS GREAT!
TRICERATOPS TRAIL
IT'S THE ONLY FRUIT YOU CAN EAT AND WASH YOUR FACE WITH, TOO!
WHERE DID MY KITE GO?
I'M HUNGRY!
LET'S FLOAT DOWN FOR A CLOSER LOOK!
WHAT DID YOU BRING TO THIS PICNIC?
MY APPETITE!
SOMETHING SMELLS GOOD!
LET ME TEACH YOU EVERYTHING I KNOW ABOUT BASEBALL.
OKAY! I HAVE A FEW MINUTES!
PLEASE DO NOT FEED THE PIZZA DELIVERY DINO!
THIS CORN IS DELICIOUS!
THAT'S BECAUSE IT'S HAND SHUCKED!
DID YOU BAKE THIS?
THAT DEPENDS ...DO YOU LIKE IT?
YOU'RE DRINKING BARBECUE SAUCE!
THE ICED TEA TASTES WEIRD AND IT'S SO THICK!
WHO ARE YOU E-MAILING?
THE GROCERY STORE. I THINK WE NEED MORE FOOD!

A DAY AT
DINO-LAND

FIND THESE ITEMS:

- ☐ Bone
- ☐ Bow tie
- ☐ Fire hydrant
- ☐ Fish
- ☐ Flower
- ☐ Flower pot
- ☐ Football
- ☐ Heart
- ☐ Hot-air balloon
- ☐ Necktie
- ☐ Net
- ☐ Pencil
- ☐ Periscope
- ☐ Pick
- ☐ Pizza delivery dino
- ☐ Plunger
- ☐ Screwdriver
- ☐ Shark fin
- ☐ Shovel
- ☐ Skier
- ☐ Sled
- ☐ Sunglasses
- ☐ Suspenders
- ☐ Tire
- ☐ Turtle

VOLCANO LAND
T-REX TOWER OF TERROR
AFTER THIS, LET'S GO ON THE GIGANTO-SAURUS-GO-ROUND!
I'M DIZZY JUST HEARING ABOUT IT!
CAMPOSAURUS GROUNDS
TRICERATOPS TOWN
IT WAS ONLY THE SHUTTLE BUS RIDE FROM THE PARKING LOT!
WHO ORDERED THIS PIZZA?
THAT LAST RIDE REALLY SCARED ME!
IN THE OLD DAYS THIS WAS ALL SWAMP LAND!!
WOW! THAT MUST HAVE BEEN GREAT!
LEAPING LIZARDS LAGOON
CARNIVOROUS CAFE
THE DINO 5
IN CONCERT NEXT WEEK
WHY IS EVERY RIDE FOLLOWED BY A TRIP TO THE GIFT SHOP?
UNDER CONSTRUCTION
DO NOT ENTER!
RUN-AWAY RHOETOSAURUS

DINO-5... IN CONCERT

FIND THESE ITEMS:

- ☐ Accordion
- ☐ Apple
- ☐ Arrow
- ☐ Astronaut
- ☐ Bandanna
- ☐ Basketball
- ☐ Bell
- ☐ Beret
- ☐ Cane
- ☐ Carrot
- ☐ Crayon
- ☐ Empty birdcage
- ☐ Fish
- ☐ Hearts (3)
- ☐ Key
- ☐ Light bulb
- ☐ Lost balloon
- ☐ Monocle
- ☐ Moon face
- ☐ Moustache
- ☐ Paintbrush
- ☐ Pear
- ☐ Pencil
- ☐ Pizza delivery dino
- ☐ Sailor cap
- ☐ Seal
- ☐ Straw
- ☐ Sunglasses
- ☐ Teapot
- ☐ Thermometer
- ☐ Top hat
- ☐ Whistler

FEEL FREE TO STOMP ALONG!
SHAKE YOUR TAIL AND ROAR!!
DO YOU ENJOY GOOD MUSIC?
YES, BUT I CAME TO THE CONCERT ANYWAY!!
DINO ROCKS
I LOVE THIS GROUP...THEY REMIND ME OF A TOOTHACHE I ONCE HAD!
I THOUGHT WE WERE GOING TO A WRESTLING MATCH.
I THOUGHT THESE TICKETS WERE FOR ADMISSION TO DINO-LAND!
THE MAIN THING WRONG WITH THIS CONCERT IS THAT WE'RE FACING THE STAGE!
WHO ORDERED A PIZZA?
BEDROCK LOVES DINO-5
ARE YOU HERE TO SEE THE CONCERT?
NO, I'M HERE FOR NEXT WEEK'S HOCKEY GAME...I'M A LITTLE EARLY!
THEIR MUSIC MAKES ME MOVE!
ME, TOO... TOWARD THE EXIT!!
YES, THERE'S DENNY, DANNY, DONNY, DARREN AND RALPH!
THEIR MUSIC IS CONTAGIOUS!
YES, I FEEL SICK ALREADY!
I PLAY GUITAR!
I PLAY THE RADIO!
GETTING YOUR SHOES ON IN THE MORNING MUST BE VERY DIFFICULT!
I DIG DINO 5
I THINK I'M ON THE WRONG PAGE OF THIS BOOK!

LAST ONE IN IS A
ROTTENSAURUS EGG

FIND THESE ITEMS:

- ☐ Balloons (2)
- ☐ Baseball caps (4)
- ☐ Bird
- ☐ Book
- ☐ Boombox
- ☐ Bone
- ☐ Bowling ball
- ☐ Fire hydrant
- ☐ Flashlight
- ☐ Football
- ☐ Golf club
- ☐ Hammer
- ☐ Horseshoe
- ☐ Ice-cream cone
- ☐ Lamp
- ☐ Mushroom
- ☐ Paper airplane
- ☐ Periscopes (2)
- ☐ Pizza delivery dino
- ☐ Ring
- ☐ Sailor cap
- ☐ Shark fins (2)
- ☐ Starfish
- ☐ Sunglasses (2)
- ☐ Telescope
- ☐ Top hat
- ☐ TV set

HOW DO I STOP?
ARE YOU GOING FISHING?
NO, I JUST LIKE CARRYING THIS POLE WITH ME WHEREVER I GO!
TO STAY COOL!
WHY DO YOU GO TO A CROWDED BEACH WITH NO SHADE ON THE HOTTEST DAY OF THE YEAR?
SNOW SHOVELS FOR SALE
WHAT WEATHER CHANNEL HAVE YOU BEEN WATCHING?
THE SUN REALLY BRINGS OUT THE COLORS IN MY SKIN!
DOES THIS UMBRELLA LEAK?
ONLY WHEN IT RAINS!
THE WATER WAS SO CROWDED EARLIER TODAY.
I KNOW! I HAD TO DIVE IN THREE TIMES BEFORE I GOT WET!
THIS IS GOING TO LOOK REALLY COOL ONCE I'M ACTUALLY IN THE WATER!
THE SUN IS DOING WONDERS TO MY SCALES.
THE SAND IS HOT!!
I WANTED TO GO WATER SKIING BUT I COULDN'T FIND A LAKE WITH A SLOPE!
IT WAS SO HOT AND HUMID LAST NIGHT THAT MY WATERBED STARTED TO BOIL!
ARE YOU LAUGHING AT MY BATHING SUIT?
NO! I'M LAUGHING AT YOU!
VISIT THE CRETACEOUS CAVES
IGUANA INLET

SCHOOL-YARDASAURUS

FIND THESE ITEMS:

- ☐ Balloon
- ☐ Banana peel
- ☐ Beret
- ☐ Bones (2)
- ☐ Bow tie
- ☐ Broom
- ☐ Butterfly
- ☐ Camera
- ☐ Coonskin cap
- ☐ Drum
- ☐ Drum major
- ☐ Eyeglasses (2)
- ☐ Fish
- ☐ Heart
- ☐ Hot dog
- ☐ Juggler
- ☐ Kite
- ☐ Lit candle
- ☐ Lollipop
- ☐ Lost cookie
- ☐ Lost sneakers
- ☐ Mailbox
- ☐ Paper airplane
- ☐ Pizza delivery dino
- ☐ Sailor cap
- ☐ Skate
- ☐ Star
- ☐ Sunglasses
- ☐ Tennis racket
- ☐ Tuba
- ☐ Yo-yo

IS IT BETTER TO WRITE A BOOK REPORT ON A FULL OR EMPTY STOMACH?
I THINK IT'S BETTER TO WRITE A BOOK REPORT ON PAPER!
WHO ORDERED THE PIZZA?
ME!
ME!
I DID!
IS THAT A FOOTBALL?
NO! SOMEONE SAT ON MY BASKETBALL!
I WANT HIM ON OUR TEAM!
COACH
I SPENT SO MANY YEARS IN THE SIXTH GRADE THAT EVERYONE THOUGHT I WAS THE TEACHER.
HOW DID YOU DO ON THIS MORNING'S TEST?
THE QUESTIONS WERE EASY... IT WAS THE ANSWERS THAT WERE HARD!
GOING TO PLAY TENNIS?
NO, I'M USING THIS AS A FLY SWATTER!
HAVE YOU EVER EATEN IN THE SCHOOL'S CAFETERIA?
NO WAY... I'VE NEVER BEEN THAT HUNGRY!
DO YOU TAKE THE SCHOOL BUS?
NO, I LET THE DRIVER TAKE ME!
MOBY DINO
I SPEND MORE TIME IN THE PRINCIPAL'S OFFICE THAN A CHALK SALESPERSON.
I'M A GRADUATE.

STAND-UP DINO

FIND THESE ITEMS:

- ☐ Airplane
- ☐ Anchor
- ☐ Apple
- ☐ Barrel
- ☐ Baseball bat
- ☐ Binoculars
- ☐ Bone
- ☐ Burned-out bulb
- ☐ Candle
- ☐ Chicken
- ☐ Clothespin
- ☐ Cups (5)
- ☐ Earring
- ☐ Fish (2)
- ☐ Football
- ☐ Heart
- ☐ Hot dog
- ☐ Kite
- ☐ Mailbox
- ☐ Monocle
- ☐ Moustache
- ☐ Pencils (2)
- ☐ Pizza delivery dino
- ☐ Sailboat
- ☐ Sled
- ☐ Sunglasses

COMING SOONER!
BARNASAURUS
HO-HO-WHO?
TONIGHT'S DINNER SPECIAL IS CHICKEN ON A ROLL.
IS THAT A BIRD THAT TELLS JOKES?
I CAN'T EAT WITH THAT GUY UP THERE.
WHO'S THE COMEDIAN WHO ORDERED A PIZZA?
LET ME GUESS, HE ORDERED IT WITH EXTRA HAM!
ARE WE SUPPOSED TO CLAP WHEN HE'S FINISHED?
THIS COMEDIAN IS B.C.— BEFORE COMEDY!
I'M LAUGHING ON THE INSIDE.
THIS COMEDIAN TALKS SO MUCH THAT HE COULD GIVE AN ASPIRIN A HEADACHE!
DO YOU HEAR THESE JOKES?
I HEAR THEM. THESE EARS AREN'T PAINTED ON!
I WANT TO BE A COMEDIAN, TOO.
WHY ARE YOU WRITING DOWN HIS JOKES?
SOMEONE TURN OFF HIS MICROPHONE.
HE SHOULD BE EXTINCT!
HE'S FUNNIER WHEN YOU LOOK THROUGH THESE!
I HOPE HE DOESN'T START SINGING.
MAYBE WE SHOULD START SINGING VERY LOUDLY!
I DON'T KNOW WHAT'S WORSE, THE COMIC OR THE FOOD?
CAN I GET YOU SOMETHING?
YES! A NEW COMEDIAN!
LET ME CALL THE BABYSITTER AND TELL HER WE'LL BE HOME EXTRA EARLY TONIGHT.
I WANT TO GO HOME!
ON WHAT-AMERICA'S MOST WANTED?

MUSEUM-SAURUS

FIND THESE ITEMS:

- ☐ Arrow
- ☐ Astronaut
- ☐ Bib
- ☐ Broom
- ☐ Camera
- ☐ Cane
- ☐ Crack
- ☐ Crown
- ☐ Dart
- ☐ Eyeglasses
- ☐ Fish
- ☐ Flower
- ☐ Golf club
- ☐ Heart
- ☐ Hourglass
- ☐ Menu
- ☐ Moustache
- ☐ Nail
- ☐ Pencils (3)
- ☐ Pizza delivery dino
- ☐ Rock
- ☐ Roll
- ☐ Telescope
- ☐ Toothbrush
- ☐ Top hat
- ☐ Umbrella
- ☐ Volcano
- ☐ Yo-yo

ARE YOU HERE AGAIN?
EVEN THE DUST IS OLD!
DOES THIS MUSEUM HAVE ANYTHING FROM THE FUTURE?
THIS WOULD BE A GREAT PLACE TO PLAY HIDE-AND-GO-SEEK!
GERTIE
ALL THIS LEARNING IS MAKING ME HUNGRY!
IS THIS WHERE THE TOUR STARTS?
VISIT YOUR LOCAL MUSEUM.
I DIDN'T KNOW THIS MUSEUM HAD AN ASTRONAUT EXHIBIT!
THEY DON'T! I'M LOST!!
NO! THIS IS WHERE IT ENDS!
TOUR
WHAT TIME IS IT?
THE TIMEPIECE COLLECTION IS ON THE THIRD FLOOR.
IS THAT A SECURITY CAMERA?
NO, THEY'RE TAKING PICTURES OF US TO COMMEMORATE OUR DAY AT THE MUSEUM!
HAS THERE ALWAYS BEEN HISTORY?
I INVENTED FIRE!
THERE IS A FINE LINE BETWEEN ARTIFACTS ...AND JUNK! OOPS!
FIRST ROCK
SOME OF THIS LONG-FORGOTTEN STUFF WOULD BE BETTER OFF FORGOTTEN.
FIRST ROLL
IS THIS ANCIENT TRASH?
NO, I THINK IT'S FRESH.
TRASH
?

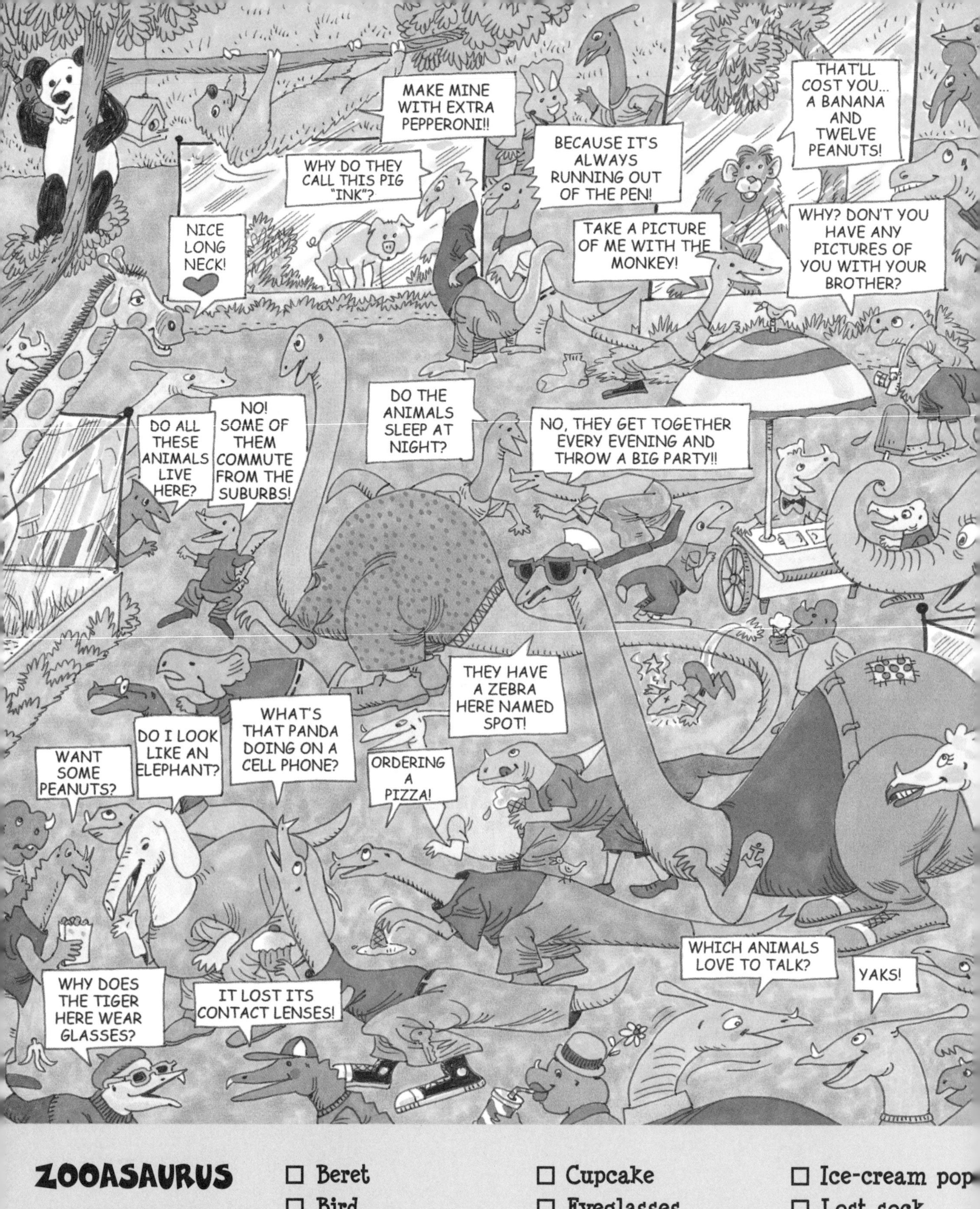

ZOOASAURUS

FIND THESE ITEMS:

- ☐ Anchor tattoo
- ☐ Banana peel
- ☐ Baseball cap
- ☐ Beret
- ☐ Bird
- ☐ Birdhouse
- ☐ Bow tie
- ☐ Camera
- ☐ Cell phone
- ☐ Cupcake
- ☐ Eyeglasses
- ☐ Fallen ice-cream cone
- ☐ Flower
- ☐ Heart
- ☐ Ice-cream pop
- ☐ Lost sock
- ☐ Star
- ☐ Sunglasses (2)

OUCH!